High-Intensity Bodybuildi

Greg DeFerro trains his triceps in the high-intensity fashion.

Lee Haney's physique looks impressive from all angles.

High-Intensity Bodybuilding

For Massive Muscles Fast

Nautilus training principles
applied to free weights and conventional equipment

By Ellington Darden, Ph.D.

Director of Research
Nautilus Sports/Medical Industries

Photography by Chris Lund

A Perigee Book

**Other Books of Interest
By Ellington Darden, Ph.D.**

Strength-Training Principles
Especially for Women
How to Lose Body Fat
Nutrition for Athletes
Conditioning for Football
The Superfitness Handbook
The Darden Technique for Weight Loss
The Athlete's Guide to Sports Medicine
The Nautilus Nutrition Book
The Nautilus Bodybuilding Book
The Nautilus Woman
How to Look Terrific in a Bathing Suit
The Nautilus Handbook for Young Athletes
The New Nautilus Book
The Nautilus Advanced Bodybuilding Book

Warning!
The high-intensity routines in this book are intended only for healthy men and women. People with health problems should not follow these routines without a physician's approval. Before beginning any exercise or dietary program, always consult with your doctor.

Acknowledgments
Special appreciation is extended to the following gyms: Gold's Gym of Venice, California; World Gym of Santa Monica, California; Mr. Fitness of Toronto, Canada; Gold's Gym of Toronto, Canada; Baltic Gym of Malmö, Sweden; and Busek's Gym of Munich, West Germany.

Perigee Books
are published by
The Putnam Publishing Group
200 Madison Avenue, New York, N.Y. 10016

Library of Congress Cataloging in Publication Data

Darden, Ellington, 1943–
High-intensity bodybuilding.

1. Weight lifting.   2. Weight lifting—Equipment
and supplies.   3. Physical fitness.   I. Title.
GV546.D27   1984   796.4'1'028   84-19010
ISBN 0-399-51103-2

Photography by Chris Lund
Designed by Martin Moskof

Printed in the United States of America

Contents

Preface

Every day there are requests at the Muscle Shop in Toronto for factual bodybuilding books," Chris Lund told me as we sat talking in my office. We had just finished several long days shooting hundreds of photographs of Boyer Coe for *The Nautilus Advanced Bodybuilding Book.* "Ell, your Nautilus books are the best in the business, but there's something missing. Do you know what I mean?"

"What's that, Chris?" I inquired.

"There're still a lot of bodybuilders out there unable and just not lucky enough to train with Nautilus equipment," he replied.

"You're right, Chris," I said. "Many trainees have been urging me to write a bodybuilding book that applies Nautilus principles to free weights."

(Left) In each of his workouts, Greg DeFerro tries to increase the number of repetitions or the amount of weight. *(Above)* Some of the most inspiring training pictures of all time were taken by Artie Zeller in 1969. Above is a grouping of some of Zeller's best photos as they appeared in the pages of *Muscle Builder* magazine.

"Bodybuilders today are hungry for hard-hitting information," said Chris, "and they simply don't get the whole truth from the muscle magazines."

"You're right again," I answered as I thumbed through one of the latest muscle magazines. "Just look at the contents page. Everything looks like warmed-over stew. Even the occasional new idea seems watered down with commercialism."

"And check out the photography," Chris challenged.

"Well, it's certainly flashy with all the full-color pictures and the dramatic layouts," I countered.

"But see how most of the pictures have a very plastic and posed look to them," Chris noted.

"Why's that?" I asked, scanning through the pages.

"It's the unavoidable result of using color photography," answered Chris knowingly. "The lighting is much more critical with color film than with black-and-white. As a result you can't capture the intensity and action that are present during the actual workouts of the champions. Everything has to be lit and relit, posed and reposed to get the color just right. The realism, therefore, is completely lost."

"Remember those black-and-white shots that were taken ten to fifteen years ago of Arnold, Franco, Zane, and Draper all training together at the old Gold's Gym?" I recalled enthusiastically.

"Exactly! Those pictures were taken by Artie Zeller back in 1969. Nothing was posed. Artie worked out at Gold's, and he always carried a Nikon in his gym bag. He couldn't have been there at a more exciting time. Arnold was at the gym almost every day, and Artie got the best training shots I've ever seen. The photos were magic, bloody magic! They kept me and many other British bodybuilders inspired enough to keep training on many a cold and dreary day back in England."

"Yep, they inspired me too, as well as thousands of others."

"Nothing like it has been done since. Just think," rambled Chris, "a whole new generation of bodybuilders has never seen honest, high-intensity action shots of the champions training. That's why for the last few years I've done my best to capture that realism and excitement on film."

As I looked over Chris's amazing photographs I found myself saying "Are you thinking the same thing I am, Chris?" Somehow we both smiled at the same time.

"Let's do it!" said Chris as his eyes sparkled with enthusiasm.

That night, August 10, 1983, *High-Intensity Bodybuilding* was conceived. Our goals were to provide trainees with factual information about muscle building and to illustrate the guidelines and routines with high-intensity training pictures of the champions in action.

Since 1977, Chris Lund has attended most of the professional physique contests in the world. He has photographed all the current champions, both in competition and in training, and many of those pictures are used throughout this book.

Lund's dynamic picture of Scott Wilson on the front cover summarizes perfectly the theme of *High-Intensity Bodybuilding.* For a more massive body, you must force your muscles to grow. Forcing your muscles to grow requires high-intensity exercise. High-intensity exercise is hard—brutally hard. It is not fun, and the lack of fun is evident on Scott's face.

High-intensity exercise, however, is the most effective form of bodybuilding ever invented. But the beauty is that it won't take you years to get the results you're seeking. Results are evident after only a few workouts, and results are very significant within only a few months.

The book is in two parts. Part I, "High-Intensity Concepts," features the workout of one of the greatest physiques of all time, Tom Platz. Chris Lund calls Tom the hardest-training bodybuilder alive. Following Platz's super-high-intensity workout, you'll learn how to apply intensity, progression, proper form, duration, and frequency to your own training sessions for maximum results.

Part II, "High-Intensity Routines," describes tried-and-proved training cycles for your major body parts. For example, you'll read about Sergio Oliva's thighs, Bertil Fox's chest, Scott Wilson's shoulders, Casey Viator's arms, and Frank Zane's midsection. You're sure to discover a few *secrets* in these chapters.

Get ready for hard-hitting information, inspiring photography, and the most result-producing routines you'll ever experience.

Get ready for *High-Intensity Bodybuilding.*

Ellington Darden, Ph.D.
Lake Helen, Florida

Dr. Ellington Darden holds B.S. and M.S. degrees from Baylor University and a Ph.D. from Florida State University. He has written over 230 articles on physical fitness and 22 books. His *Nautilus Bodybuilding Book* was recently ranked in the #1 position of the American Booksellers Association's top ten sports paperbacks.

Part I

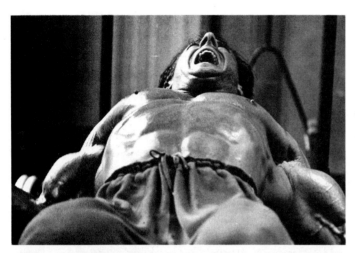

High-Intensity Concepts

Chapter 1

"Mr. High Intensity"

(*Left*) Mr. Universe Tom Platz struggles to get the last repetition in a set of incline presses.
(*Above*) After a set of full squats, Tom contracts his quadriceps for Lou Ferrigno, better known as The Incredible Hulk.

(*Top*) Tom Platz and his assistants have just lifted the 305-pound barbell to the top position of the press behind neck. Tom will now lower the barbell slowly to a count of ten behind his neck. (*Bottom*) Once the barbell is behind Platz's neck, the assistants prepare to lift the weight back to the top position for another slow negative repetition.

That's it, lock it out! Now lower it slowly," cried one of Tom Platz's training partners.

Tom lowered the incredible weight behind his neck slowly to a count of ten. During the lowering, his face turned almost purple, his neck bulged like a giant cobra, and his triceps and deltoids looked as if they were ready to burst from his skin.

At the bottom position, no words were spoken. Tom simply nodded his head, which signaled his assistants that he was ready for them to help him get the barbell back overhead.

"Up," said the assistant on the right, and with a tremendous surge of energy from all three, the 305-pound barbell was back at the top position. "Give me ten seconds, Tom," the assistant shouted.

For his final set, Tom often performs as many presses as possible with 115 pounds.

Seated calf raise.
Bent-over raise.
Full squat.

Incline triceps extension.
Triceps pressdown on lat machine.
Alternate biceps curl.

Inch by inch Platz lowered the 305-pound weight behind his neck in a negative-only manner. His partners did most of the positive work and he did the negative work. Up again and lower, up again and lower.

Every repetition looked like Tom's last, but somehow he kept lowering the barbell in perfect form—that is, until the ninth. Rather than taking eight to ten seconds to lower, the ninth repetition was completed in about four or five seconds.

"Okay," one of the assistants challenged. "This next rep is the most important." Up went the barbell to the top position. "Try to stop the weight half way down. Good, now hold it there as long as you can."

Even though he was pushing upward as hard as possible, Tom couldn't hold the massive weight by himself. His partners placed their hands under the ends of the bar and helped just enough to keep the bar from moving downward. Slowly, in about three or four seconds, the barbell touched Tom's shoulders.

"Take it," Tom grimaced as the barbell was placed back into the racks. "My shoulders are on fire,"

Tom as he appeared in the 1981 Mr. Olympia in Columbus, Ohio.

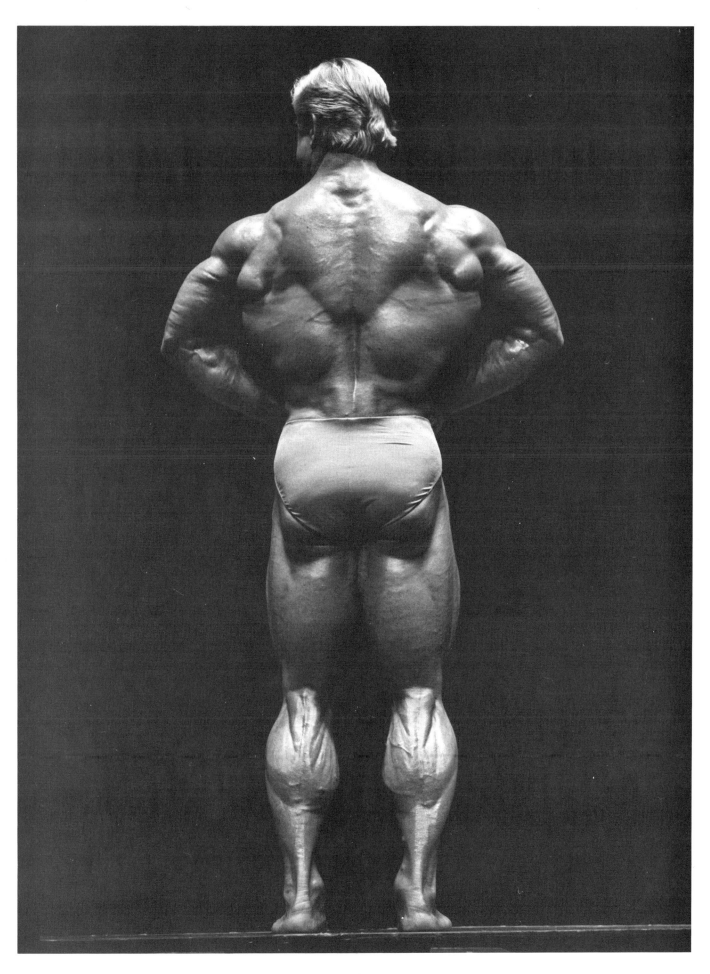

Platz moaned as he wiped the sweat from his face with the back of his hand.

Then an amazing thing happened. An ordinary bodybuilder would have rested and then moved to another exercise. But not Platz. When most trainees reach momentary muscular failure in an exercise, Tom Platz is just beginning his set.

Quickly the weight on the barbell was reduced by 50 pounds, and Tom was back bombing his shoulders with more negative-only repetitions of the same exercise. Four slow repetitions were performed strictly, and then Tom failed to control the fifth rep. Immediately the weight was reduced by 70 pounds, and another four reps were done. Because of the intense pain during the final rep, Platz screamed out loud as the barbell was lowered.

"That's it, my shoulders have had it," Tom cried as he staggered over to a bench. Sweat now covered every corner of his pulsating body. In fact, only Tom Platz knows the burning feeling that was happening inside his deltoids. In less than five minutes he had worked—no, tortured—his deltoids into growing.

And grow they did. Anyone who attended the 1981 Mr. Olympia contest will testify that Tom Platz came into his own that night. Sure, Platz has had the greatest legs in the world for a number of years. His upper body, however, had always lagged behind. Well, it didn't lag behind in Columbus, Ohio, the night of the Mr. Olympia.

"Platz was truly fantastic," remembers one prominent spectator. "Even though he placed a respectable third, he should have won. He was that good. Almost everyone in attendance was shocked at Platz's new body."

One person that wasn't shocked was Mike Mentzer.

"Platz was the one guy in Gold's Gym who trained hard all winter long," Mike said. "He went to total failure on every exercise. I remember saying to my brother Ray that this guy must really be serious.

"I didn't know what he looked like underneath his sweatsuit until I saw him getting some sun just before the contest. I couldn't believe my eyes. He'd put 12 pounds of pure muscle on his upper body alone. His delts, pecs, and lats almost equalled his incredible legs. I knew he would be unbelievable at the Olympia."

Another muscle enthusiast not the least bit surprised at the improvement of Tom Platz was top Canadian bodybuilder John Cardillo, also known for his high-intensity training methods. After visiting Gold's Gym in the winter of 1981, he recalled to Chris Lund, "Platz is training like a man possessed. I've never seen anything like it. The intensity he puts into each set has to be seen to be believed. You should go and see it for yourself."

Chris Lund did travel to California in August of 1981 to see it for himself. The photographs in this chapter were taken during Platz's actual workouts. None of them is posed.

"Tom Platz is the hardest training bodybuilder I've ever observed," said Lund, "and I've seen and photographed most of the greats. He truly deserves the title of 'Mr. High Intensity.'"

What is the secret of Tom Platz's training? How was he able to add over 12 pounds of solid muscle to his upper body in 1981?

The secret by now should be self-evident. It is *hard work*—hard work manifested in the form of *high-intensity exercise.* Tom has the ability to milk the absolute maximum out of every set of every exercise he performs. And such high-intensity training is an important component for maximum stimulation of his muscles.

But high-intensity exercise is not the only requirement for maximum muscular growth. Your muscles must be permitted to grow by keeping the total amount of exercise brief and infrequent. The next chapter will tell you why.

Tom Platz is "Mr. High Intensity."

(*Left*) Casey Viator's training partner helps him do several more repetitions of incline presses.
(*Above*) The fun part of high-intensity training is not the exercise, but the end result: larger, stronger muscles. Albert Beckles possesses some of the largest, strongest muscles in professional bodybuilding.

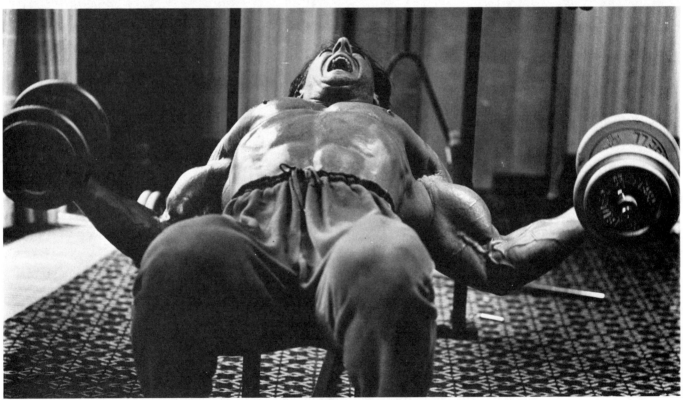

Reid Schindle is in the middle of a set of dumbbell pullovers.
Greg DeFerro employs bent-armed flies for his chest.

Tom Platz would probably define high-intensity exercise as milking the exercise for all it's worth! While this is certainly true, it is also more than that. The real pioneer in high-intensity exercise is Arthur Jones, the man behind the development of Nautilus equipment. Some of Jones's early writings contain lengthy discussions about intensity, or what he sometimes called "outright hard work."

"Have you ever vomited as a result of doing one set of barbell curls?" asks Arthur Jones. "If not, then you simply don't know what hard work is."

Arnold Schwarzenegger went through one of Jones's training sessions and remarked, "I've experienced times during a workout where I had difficulty walking. But this is the first time that I've ever had difficulty lying down."

Alternate curls are regularly done by Greg DeFerro.

Mike Mentzer, Ray Mentzer, Casey Viator, Sergio Oliva, and Boyer Coe have all experienced similar workouts under Jones's watchful eye. Their workouts were not fun! Their muscles, however, grew at a rate they had never experienced before.

On a recent visit to the Nautilus Sports/Medical Industries, top physique star Scott Wilson was put through only two exercises for his biceps: slow chin-ups followed by seated curls, each carried to both positive and negative muscular failure. From less than three minutes of exercise for his biceps, Wilson spent the next ten minutes lying on the floor recovering. "I've never seen anything like it," remarked Chris Lund, who observed the workout. "After the brief session the veins in Scott's arms looked like ¾-inch steel cables. His arms were pumped at least 1½ inches."

"The most efficient way to the top in bodybuilding," Arthur Jones says, "involves outright hard

Scott Wilson knows the pain involved in high-intensity training.
The last repetition in a set is the only one that has the potential to provide maximum intensity.

Tony Pearson and Carla Dunlap display the bodybuilding effects of high-intensity work.

work. Unfortunately, most bodybuilders aren't willing to work at the necessary level of intensity."

INTENSITY DEFINED

Maximum intensity, according to Jones, is involved only when a muscle is pulling as hard as momentarily possible, producing as much force as it is capable of producing at that moment. Intensity, however, cannot be determined by measuring output.

During a normal set of ten repetitions with a barbell, the level of intensity increases with each repetition, and is maximum only during the final repetition, and then only if the final repetition leads to a point of momentary muscular failure. If it was possible to perform an eleventh repetition, then the intensity never reached a maximum level. Maximum intensity is produced only if an exercise is carried to a point where another repetition is impossible. So we can measure maximum intensity, but only under certain circumstances.

During the first of a set of ten repetitions the intensity is low, even though the output is actually higher than during the final repetition.

If you curl a 100-pound barbell in a strict manner, performing ten repetitions and failing during the eleventh repetition, then the output is high and the intensity is low during the first repetition, and the output is low and the intensity is high during the tenth repetition. During the first repetition you were momentarily capable of lifting more weight. Thus the output was high, but it was lifted easily, so the intensity was low. During the tenth repetition you were not momentarily capable of doing more. If the weight had been any heavier, you could not have lifted it. Again the weight was lifted, but it was lifted slower. Thus the output was lower than it was during the first repetition, and, since you were working as hard as possible, the intensity was high.

It should now be obvious that intensity is a relative situation depending upon momentary ability, varying moment by moment and not directly related to output. If you could have done more but did not, then the intensity was low. But the intensity is maximum if you are doing all you can at the moment regardless of how much or how little output is actually involved.

The production of force is also related to output and can be measured, but a high level of force is not required for high intensity. In fact, if exercises are performed properly, then the maximum-intensity repetitions will actually involve less force. It is possible and desirable to have high intensity and low force at the same time. A failure to understand this simple point has led to a ridiculous situation very commonly encountered in bodybuilding programs.

HARDER, BUT SAFER

Many, perhaps most, bodybuilders avoid the final two or three repetitions in a set under the mistaken belief that they are eliminating the most dangerous repetitions. In fact, the final repetitions are actually the safest, because the output and the production of force are lower. During the final repetition you are imposing less pulling force on your muscular attachments than you were during the first few repetitions.

As a direct consequence, most bodybuilders produce results that are far below optimum. A high percentage of the muscular size and strength increases produced by exercise is a direct result of high intensity, which is involved only in the final two or three repetitions.

Several years of exercising by stopping three repetitions short of a point of momentary failure will not produce results equal to what can be produced in a few weeks by an otherwise exactly similar training program that carries to the point of momentary failure.

The final two or three repetitions are the most productive repetitions in a set, and then only if the set proceeds to a point of failure.

The first few repetitions are merely preparation and do little in the way of increasing strength. These repetitions are of limited value because the intensity is low. The final repetitions are productive because the intensity is high.

Since the facts, simple and undeniable though they are, run directly contrary to very widespread

belief, it will be a long time before this point is understood and accepted by a high percentage of bodybuilders. In the meantime, most bodybuilding programs will consist primarily of wasted effort. Millions of man-hours of training and billions of foot-pounds of effort will be devoted to programs that produce little value.

MORE EXERCISE IS NOT BETTER

Without high intensity, gains in strength will come slowly, if at all. Trainees will lose interest from a lack of progress, and many will look elsewhere in search of some secret to more rapid size and strength increases. Numerous trainees will make the old mistake of equating more with better. When progress is less than expected, they will increase the amount of training, under the mistaken belief that

Harder, briefer exercise is the secret to making continual progress.
(*Overleaf*) Do *not* avoid the final few repetitions of any exercise. Carry each set to momentary muscular failure.

training more means training harder. In fact, all that is required is an increase in the intensity of exercise.

Most bodybuilders who do stick to a strength program for a long period of time eventually fall into a pattern of training. Their workouts are about as productive as walking cross-country on a treadmill. The intensity of their workouts is seldom high enough to stimulate strength increases, but the amount of training is so high that they remain in a constantly run-down condition.

Under such circumstances, if growth is stimulated, it will be slow in all cases and impossible in many cases. The recovery ability will be constantly forced to work as hard as possible merely to replace the large amount of energy that is required, leaving nothing as a reserve for growth.

High-intensity training and a large amount of training are mutually exclusive factors. You can have one or the other, but not both. If you double the intensity of training, then you must reduce the amount of training by more than 80 percent to compensate for the increased intensity. If not, then you will produce losses in strength instead of gains.

PROVING A POINT

Since it is difficult to measure an intensity level less than maximum, how do we prove that point, how can we test such a theory? Very easily. Determine how much weight you can curl for ten repetitions in perfect form with an eleventh repetition being impossible.

Let us assume this weight turns out to be 100 pounds. Then use exactly half as much weight, 50 pounds, and perform twenty sets of curls with this reduced weight during each of three weekly training sessions. After six months of such training, with no other training of any kind, you should test your ability with 100 pounds again. Don't be surprised if you are actually weaker than you were at the start. A large amount of low-intensity exercise did very little for increasing strength, probably nothing, and may even have produced losses.

Now double the weight, go back to the 100 pounds, and perform twenty sets of as many repetitions as possible. Again follow a program of three weekly workouts, twenty sets of curls in each workout, and no other exercise. You should not be surprised that you lose strength rapidly and grow steadily weaker—at least, you would lose strength if such a comparison were made using exercises for all of the major muscular structures in the body.

A large amount of low-intensity exercise will do little to increase strength, and a large amount of high-intensity exercise will produce losses in strength. But if you reduce the number of sets to only one or two, instead of twenty, and double the weight used during the large amount of low-intensity exercise, then rapid and steady increases in strength are produced. These increases continue as long as the intensity is as high as momentarily possible during each set and as long as each set is continued to a point of failure. In such a case, you are performing only 20 percent as much exercise—10 percent as many sets, but with twice as much weight. Obviously, then, the amount of exercise is reduced 80 percent compared to the low-intensity exercise program. Yet the results are much better.

In spite of all the evidence, most trainees still persist in doing more when they should be working less but working harder. To produce good results from exercise, bodybuilders must work harder, and if they work harder, then they must work less.

Chapter 3

Bertil Fox has always believed in performing a few basic exercises with as much weight as possible.

Exercise Selection

Basically, there are two types of bodybuilding exercises: single-joint and multiple-joint. Single-joint exercises require movement around only one joint. Multiple-joint exercises involve movement around two or more joints.

Examples of single-joint exercises are the biceps curl, triceps extension, and calf raise. Such exercises, if performed strictly, isolate a given muscle group such as the biceps, triceps, and gastrocnemius.

The bench press, squat, and deadlift are multiple-joint exercises. In the deadlift, for example, you have movement around at least five joints: ankle, knee, hip, lower back, and shoulder. The deadlift involves some work for many muscles, but it does not work any one muscle group thoroughly.

Lee Haney, 1982 Mr. America and Mr. Universe, demonstrates three variations of rowing exercises: T-bar, barbell, and cable.

EVALUATING AN EXERCISE

Both single- and multiple-joint exercises should be used in a successful bodybuilding program. But naturally, some exercises are more productive than others. Arthur Jones says the value of an exercise may be judged according to the following considerations:

1. It should isolate a large muscle by working the muscle throughout its possible range of movement. Isolation exercises are usually single-joint movements.

2. It should involve as many muscle groups as possible. Such exercises entail multiple-joint actions.

3. It should provide resistance in the position of full-muscular contraction. An exercise that permits locking out under the resistance is inferior to an exercise in which the resistance remains constant.

4. It should involve as much total muscle mass as possible. In general, the greater the mass of the involved muscles, the greater the value of the exercise.

EXAMINING THE PROBLEMS

If we consider those required characteristics for a productive exercise, it becomes obvious that at least some of them are mutually exclusive. To satisfy one of the requirements, it is frequently necessary to make use of an exercise that provides none of, or at least not all of, the other requirements.

For example, the full squat involves a large mass of muscle, which is an advantage. It is also a multiple-joint exercise, involving a number of major muscular structures working together and this is another advantage. But it is not full-range movement, since there is no resistance during the last part of the exercise as you come fully erect. Since you can lock out in the fully erect position, there is no resistance in the position of full contraction of the involved muscles.

Also, in a squat the point of maximum resistance is encountered shortly after the start of the upward movement when the midline of the thighs is parallel with the floor. At that point, the involved muscles are not in their strongest positions. Thus you encounter the most resistance when the muscles are not as capable of handling it as they are later during the movement. The resistance you can handle in a squat is limited by the strength of the muscles in that particular position, not their strongest position. The muscles will be worked to their maximum ability in that one position but will not encounter enough resistance in other positions.

Similar problems are encountered in almost all conventional exercises. In spite of these limitations, it is still possible to outline a training routine made up of a few basic, heavy exercises that will produce very good results. The most common mistake is including too many exercises, and the unavoidable result is that the overall recovery ability of the system cannot meet the requirement for both full recovery from the workouts and additional growth at the same time. Under such circumstances, growth will be impossible, or very slow at best.

RANGE OF MOVEMENT AND POWER PRODUCTION

Another valid means of determining the relative values of similar exercises is to compare the actual distances of movement. Everything else being equal, the greater the distance of movement, the greater the value of the exercise. For example, a standing press is a much better exercise than a bench press primarily because the distance of movement is greater in a standing press.

Therefore, it should also be obvious that the style of performance that provides the greatest distance of movement is the best. For this reason, bench presses with a reasonably narrow grip are more productive than the same movements with a wider grip.

Another method of judging the value of exercises involves a comparison of the power production in one exercise to the power production in another. But in this case we must be very sure that we know exactly what power really is and what it is not. The amount of resistance involved is only one of three factors that must be considered. We must also consider the vertical distance the resistance is moved and the speed of movement or the time involved.

The leg curl is a single-joint exercise that involves the hamstrings throughout a long range of movement. The deadlift is a multiple-joint exercise that provides mid-range work for many muscles.

(*Top Left*) Shoulder shrugs activate the muscles of the neck and upper back. (*Top Right*) The incline press involves a greater range of movement than the bench press. But the overhead press provides even greater movement than the incline press. (*Bottom Left*) A variation of the overhead press is done with dumbbells. (*Bottom Right*) Moving the hands closer together in the above picture would improve the range of movement and thus the effectiveness of the behind neck pulldown.

Larry Jackson displays a magnificent upper body in this front lat spread.

Most people assume that more power is required in a bench press than in a standing press. In fact, quite the opposite is true. While the amount of resistance may well be greater in a bench press than it is in a standing press, the other two factors are both reduced in the bench press. The distance and the speed of movement are both less in a bench press than they are in a standing press. And in almost all cases, more power is actually produced in a maximum standing press than in a maximum bench press.

But again, the style of performance is an important factor. All exercises should be performed in a style that results in maximum power production by the muscles you are trying to develop. A jerk-press will produce a faster speed of movement and thus more power than a military press. But most of the power is not produced by the muscles you are usually trying to develop: the triceps, the deltoids, and the trapezius.

This does not mean cheating methods should never be employed. They should be, in almost every set of every exercise—but only after a point of failure has been reached while performing the movements with good form. Two or three cheating repetitions performed at the end of a set of several repetitions performed in perfect style will force the muscles to work beyond a point of normal failure. It is important that such permissible cheating be restricted to the minimum required to complete the movements. Cheat to make the last two or three repetitions possible, not to make them easy. Properly performed, the cheated repetitions also should be brutally hard.

BEST EXERCISES

The best conventional exercises are listed below. They should form the backbone of all your bodybuilding programs. The majority of these exercises will be fully described in later chapters.

Single-Joint Exercises

Calf raise	Lateral raise	Triceps extension
Leg extension	Front raise	Bent-over triceps extension
Leg curl	Bent-over raise	Lat machine pressdown
Trunk curl	Straight-armed pullover	Wrist curl
Reverse trunk curl	Biceps curl	Reverse wrist curl
Shoulder shrug	Reverse curl	

Multi-Joint Exercises

Squat	Dip	Decline press
Leg press	Overhead press	Incline press
Hack squat	Press behind neck	Bent-armed fly
Sissy squat	Upright row	Bent-armed pullover
Stiff-legged deadlift	Bent-over row	Lat machine pulldown
Chin-up	Bench press	

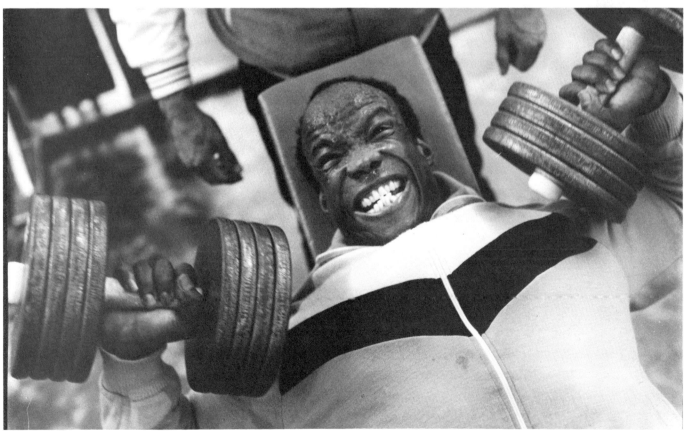

Always perform as many repetitions as possible in all your exercises.
A unique picture of Mr. Universe, Albert Beckles, as he does presses on the incline bench.

least approaching your momentary limit is an absolute requirement. Yet most bodybuilders seldom continue an exercise to a point anywhere near the required intensity of effort. Then they attempt to justify their easier styles of training by performing more exercises or more sets of each exercise.

More exercise, regardless of the amount, will never produce the results that are possible from harder exercise. If much additional exercise is employed, then growth will be impossible even if growth stimulation is being produced. In practice, most bodybuilders quickly fall into a training rut in which their workouts almost totally deplete their recovery ability. Thus, it takes them years to attain the same results that could have been produced in months.

HARD AND BRIEF

In simple terms, best results seem to come when the exercises are as hard as possible but as brief as possible. Unfortunately, this statement is subject to misunderstanding. For example, "as hard as possible but as brief as possible" could mean one repetition of one exercise with maximum intensity of effort. In practice, the result of such a program would be far less than optimum. For one thing, you could never be quite sure that the one repetition actually was as hard as possible. You would be required to guess the exact level of existing strength, and you would seldom, if ever, select the correct poundage. If you guessed too high, then the attempt would fail. If you guessed too low, then it would not actually be a maximum effort.

A weight should be selected that will permit the performance of at least eight repetitions but not

The dynamic bodies of Rachel McLish and Bill Grant are a result of excellent genetics and progressive exercise.

more than twenty, and each set should be carried to the point of momentary muscular failure—to a point at which additional movement is impossible.

The first repetition of such a set will seem quite easy—but in fact, it is the hardest and most dangerous repetition. You are strongest during the first repetition, and the repetitions coming after the first merely seem harder because you are growing progressively weaker. For that reason, the first repetition should be performed at a slow speed to reduce the possibility of injury. The first three or four repetitions of a set should be performed in a similar manner. Later repetitions should be performed at a somewhat faster speed, but still smoothly. By the time you reach the end of a correctly executed set, you should be moving as rapidly as possible, which in fact will be a very slow speed of movement.

AS MANY REPETITIONS AS POSSIBLE

A guide figure of a particular number of repetitions, usually from twelve to twenty, should be selected. A set should not be terminated simply because a particular number of repetitions has been performed. Instead, complete as many repetitions as you can in good form, then cheat at least two more, and stop only when additional movement becomes impossible. If the number of repetitions performed in correct form is less than the guide figure, then use the same amount of resistance during the next workout. If you can perform twelve repetitions or more in good form (twelve being the guide figure in this example), then the weight should be increased by approximately 5 percent for the next workout.

You might, for example, be using 100 pounds in the barbell curl. During your first workout with this weight, you might be able to do eight repetitions in good form, then fail during an attempt to perform a ninth. In that case, you should then perform another two cheated repetitions—using just enough body swing to make the additional two possible. You should not cheat enough to make those extra repetitions easy, just enough to make them barely possible.

During a later workout, you might be successful with nine repetitions in correct form with the same resistance. If so, the resistance should remain unchanged. Eventually you will be able to perform twelve repetitions or more—and all in good form. This is your signal to increase the resistance in that particular exercise during the next workout. You should add 5 pounds to the weight being used, bringing your curling resistance to a new total of 105 pounds. During the next workout, using the increased resistance, you might find that you could perform only eight repetitions in good form. Again, you should cheat two additional repetitions. Eventually you will be able to perform twelve or more in good form with 105 pounds. Increase the resistance by another 5 pounds again—to a new total of 110 pounds.

If you continually strive to increase both the number of repetitions performed and the resistance employed, you will eventually find yourself capable of curling 150 or more pounds for eight or nine repetitions in good form. When you can perform a set with 150 pounds, your arms will be far larger than they were when you could use only 100 pounds in the same exercise.

TRUE PROGRESSION

Such training is progressive, the basic principle involved in any form of worthwhile physical training. The very name of the game seems to have been forgotten by most current bodybuilders, who seldom make any real efforts in the direction of true progression. Instead, they select a given amount of resistance and then perform a certain number of repetitions—stopping well short of the point of failure. No amount of such training will ever produce anything approaching the results that are possible from a small amount of progressive exercise.

This much is evident: If you are not willing to perform progressive exercise—and it certainly is not an easy style of training—then you will never produce the final results that are possible. Your rate of progress will be far below its potential.

No one can endure a large amount of such training. Training with the intensity of effort required for attaining good results is very hard—and must be very brief.

Chapter 5

James Gaubert uses strict form on dumbbell curls to isolate his biceps.

Proper Form

Mohamed Makkawy is a believer in proper form in posing as well as exercise.

The form, or style of performance, required for maximum results from weight training is much discussed but little understood. Proper form includes speed of movement, range of movement, momentary muscular failure, and supervision.

SPEED OF MOVEMENT

A force plate is a delicate measuring device that can be connected to an oscilloscope. Accurate measurements of force during a barbell exercise can be recorded by standing on the plate as you perform an exercise. As recorded on the oscilloscope screen, the difference between the performance of fast and slow repetitions is dramatic.

Negative repetitions may be performed with a heavy dumbbell by lifting the weight with both arms and lowering it with only one arm.

Fast repetitions show as peaks and drops on the oscilloscope. These peaks and drops indicate that, while being lifted, a 100-pound barbell can exert from more than 500 pounds of force to less than zero. Such erratic force is not only unproductive as far as muscle stimulation is concerned but also very dangerous to the joints, muscles, and connective tissues.

Slow, steady repetitions show as a relatively smooth tracing on the oscilloscope. This kind of tracing indicates that the barbell's resistance is being directed properly against the muscle throughout the exercise's range of movement.

The research performed at Nautilus Sports/Medical Industries over the last fourteen years proves that slow repetitions are much more productive than fast repetitions for bodybuilding purposes. As a general rule, each repetition should be performed in approximately six seconds: two seconds to lift the weight, four seconds to lower it. The negative or lowering phase of each repetition should be emphasized.

RANGE OF MOVEMENT

The range of movement of each repetition, from stretch to contraction, should be as great as possible. When a muscle contracts even a little, it must produce movement. If it contracts fully, that muscle must produce a full range of movement. If the movement resulting from muscular contraction is less than full-range, the entire length of the muscle will not be involved in the work. Increased muscular size and shape are most likely to be achieved when the muscles have been strengthened in every position over a full range of movement.

MOMENTARY MUSCULAR FAILURE

In high-intensity exercise, it is important to work the muscle until *momentary muscular failure*. Momentary muscular failure in most barbell exercises means performing as many strict repetitions as possible and then doing several more cheating repetitions. As a result, the involved muscles are temporarily fatigued until they cannot contract positively against the weight of the barbell.

When you lift or raise a barbell, you are performing positive work and the muscle is shortening. When you lower a barbell, you are performing negative work and the muscle is lengthening. Common sense reveals that your positive strength is much less than your negative strength. Thus, when you train until momentary muscular failure, the involved muscles usually fail positively but not negatively.

It is possible, however, to work beyond positive failure. Forced repetitions can be performed with the help of a partner, as can negative repetitions.

In forced repetitions, your training partner helps you slightly by lifting on the barbell during the positive part of the exercise. He helps you just enough to get you past the sticking point. Then you lower the barbell slowly and smoothly back to the bottom position. Two or three forced repetitions may be performed at the end of a normal set of most barbell exercises. This is the first way to work beyond positive failure.

The other way is to incorporate negative repetitions into your training. For negative repetitions, your partner, or partners, must lift the barbell for you. Again it is your job to lower the barbell very slowly and smoothly to the bottom position. For best results, take a full eight to ten seconds to lower the barbell. Two or three negative repetitions may be performed in this manner after positive failure has occurred or after positive failure and forced repetitions have been performed. This last method is indeed a very intense way to train. More will be said about this training method in later chapters.

SUPERVISION

A bodybuilder is rarely able to push himself to a 100-percent effort. He may succeed in two or three exercises, but experience teaches that it is virtually impossible to do this consistently. High-intensity exercise is not easy. Properly performed, it is very demanding, and it is not surprising that few people can do it on their own. A supervisor or training partner is usually needed to urge bodybuilders to work at the required level of intensity.

Lateral raises with dumbbells provide both positive and negative work for the deltoids and upper back.

An example from the sport of running should help clarify this concept. Let us say that an athlete can run a quarter of a mile in 50 seconds. When he runs at this speed, he is making a 100-percent effort. His pain during the last 100 yards will be almost unbearable. He rationalizes, therefore, that if he slows slightly to run the distance in 55 seconds, he will probably get about 90-percent results. He reasons that if he repeats this 55-second quarter three times, he will be accomplishing more than he would by running once around the track in an all-out 100-percent effort. And it will certainly hurt less.

Actually, his reasoning is false. His three runs at 55 seconds per quarter will never yield results as great as a single all-out run that uses 100 percent of his effort. It is the 100-percent effort that forces his body to overcompensate and become stronger. Ninety percent efforts, regardless of how many times they are repeated, will never produce the results attained by one 100-percent effort.

The same principle applies to building muscular size and strength. If a bodybuilder can do eleven repetitions in a strenuous effort on a given exercise but stops at ten, he has not reached his potential. This is why supervision is so important. You simply cannot push yourself hard enough. You need a supervisor to tell you when to slow down, to hold your head back, and to relax your lower body when working your upper body. You must be urged, implored, and inspired to do the last repetition of each exercise.

MAXIMUM RESULTS

For maximum bodybuilding results, form is one of the most important factors. Never sacrifice form in an attempt to use more weight or perform more repetitions. But always use as much weight as you can, and always perform as many repetitions as you can—in good form.

Chapter 6

Scott Wilson employs negative-only dips for his arms and chest.

Negative-Only Exercise

**M**any bodybuilders make the mistake of paying too much attention to the positive part of their exercises and ignoring the negative part. They lift the weight in good form, but they lower it haphazardly.

For the purpose of increasing muscular size and strength, the negative phase is the most important. To the degree that it is possible, the negative part of the exercise should be emphasized.

ADVANTAGES OF NEGATIVE WORK

The negative phase of exercise provides the following advantages: (1) stretching, for the improvement of flexibility; (2) prestretching, for high-intensity

---

(*Left*) Casey Viator built a large part of his incredible muscle mass from negative-only training.
(*Above*) Strong training partners are necessary for getting the best results from negative exercise.

Without the back pressure of negative work, stretching would not be possible.
Negative-only presses require an assistant stationed at either end of the barbell.

muscular contraction; (3) resistance in the position of full contraction, for full-range exercise; and (4) maximum application of resistance throughout a full range of possible movement, because it is impossible to throw a weight down.

The first three advantages of negative training are easy to understand. Without the back pressure of force pulling against you at the beginning of an exercise movement, there would be nothing to stretch your muscles and improve flexibility. Without such stretching of the muscles, there would be no prestretch, which is the neurological stimulus required for high-intensity muscular contraction. With no force pulling back against you at the end of an exercise movement, there is no resistance in the position of full muscular contraction. Thus, without negative work, nothing would be done for flexibility. High-intensity work would be impossible.

The fourth advantage requires more explanation. While performing positive work, it is easy to throw the weight rather than lift it. If the upward movement is started with a jerk or if the movement is done too quickly, your muscles will not be able to keep pace with the weight. Having started with a yank, which is dangerous in itself, the muscles you seek to exercise can contribute only a little to the subsequent movement. When this happens your muscles are deprived of a most valuable phase of the exercise.

A weight that is too heavy may be impossible for you to lift properly. So instead of lifting it, you are forced to throw it. This results in an unproductive and dangerous style of training.

The weight should be as heavy as possible but not too heavy. It should be as heavy as you can handle in good form. If it is heavier than that, good form becomes impossible and injury is probable. If the weight is lighter than you can handle in good form, you are simply wasting time and futilely burning up energy. You should use as much weight as you can, while maintaining good form. You should increase the weight as often and as much as you can. But you should never increase the weight if you must sacrifice form to do so.

In reality, eager bodybuilders often start throwing the weight instead of lifting it. Usually they are under the impression that they are showing progress, since it soon becomes possible to use more weight.

By using a negative style of training, such throwing becomes unlikely. You can always drop a weight, but you cannot throw it down.

SLOW, CONTROLLED REPETITIONS

In negative-only training the weight must be lifted by somebody else; then you slowly lower the weight, performing only the negative part of the work. Jerking, yanking, heaving, throwing, and too-fast movements are thus avoided. The objective of negative exercise is to lower the weight slowly, very slowly, but without interrupting the downward movement. At the start of a negative-only exercise, you should be able to stop the downward movement if you try to, but you should not try. After six or seven repetitions you should be unable to stop the downward movement no matter how hard you try; however, you should still be able to guide it into a slow, steady, smooth descent.

Finally, after two or three more repetitions you should find it impossible to stop the weight's downward acceleration. At that moment, you should terminate the exercise.

Properly performed negative-only exercise, therefore, assures more complete exercise for the muscles because the weight is never thrown. It always moves at a smooth, steady pace.

Being involved with negative-only exercise at Nautilus Sports/Medical Industries for the last fourteen years, we have found the following exercises most productive:

Barbell Exercises

Biceps curl, standing
Bench press
Press behind neck, seated
Upright row

Shoulder shrug
Triceps extension, seated
Squat
Front squat

Dumbbell Exercises

One-armed biceps curl, seated
One-armed triceps extension, seated

Exercises with Other Equipment

Chin-up
Dip
Calf raise
Leg extension
Leg curl

THE PROBLEM OF HELPERS

Negative-only exercise is not without problems. One problem is that it is usually necessary to have somebody lift the weight for you so you can perform only the lowering part.

A few exercises can be performed in a negative-only fashion without help. Negative chins can be done by climbing into the top position using the legs, so that the arms simply lower you back down. Negative dips can be done in the same way.

A few other exercises can be done in a negative-only fashion without help. In general, however, you will need help—and finding such help is seldom easy. For most bodybuilders, a totally negative program of exercises is impractical.

TWO SECONDS UP, FOUR SECONDS DOWN

Probably the most important thing learned from practicing negative-only exercise is that most trainees have been neglecting the negative aspect of exercise and that their results have suffered as a consequence. Bodybuilders must be sure to pay careful attention to both the positive and negative parts of all exercises.

Even in normal positive-negative sets, the weight should be lifted smoothly and slowly. Then it should be lowered to the starting position even more slowly. Again, an excellent guideline to follow is that it should take two seconds to lift the resistance and four seconds to lower it—two seconds positive, four seconds negative. Doing exercises in this fashion will require you to use less weight, but it will greatly increase the results, which is what you are after. As a side benefit, this training style will almost totally eliminate the chance of injury.

Tom Platz has trained extensively with negative exercise.

Chapter 7

The Full Squat

(*Left*) Danny Fisher performs repetitions in the squat with 495 pounds.
(*Above*) The thighs of Tom Platz are capable of squatting with 600 pounds for ten repetitions.

Recently there has been a tremendous amount of controversy on the subject of full squats. According to some people, the practice of full squats is an almost certain road to destruction of the knee. According to others, full squats are the best single exercise in existence. What is the truth about squats?

DEFINING A SQUAT

First, it is important to define a full squat. In powerlifting circles, squatting is limited to a point where the tops of the thighs are parallel with the floor. But to a man with heavy legs, that is a full squat. In fact, many of the heavier powerlifters have difficulty going that low—the backs of their thighs are compressed solidly against the

Samir Bannout, Mr. Olympia 1983, recognizes the value of performing squats for developing overall muscular size.

backs of their calves long before they reach a parallel position. That is exactly why parallel rather than full squats are included as one of the three basic powerlifts. Otherwise, there would have been endless controversy between the lighter men and the heavier men about how low a squat was supposed to be. For bodybuilding purposes, the knees should be bent until the thighs start to contact the backs of the calves.

THE DANGERS OF FORCE

Competitive lifting is a dangerous sport—and this is true of both Olympic lifting and powerlifting, but for different reasons. In practicing the Olympic lifts, the suddenness of movement is the most dangerous factor. Such sudden movements, under heavy loads, impose tremendous G forces on the muscles, tendons, ligaments, and bones. In performing a clean-and-jerk with 400 pounds, a man may momentarily expose his muscles and tendons to a force that is actually ten times as heavy as the weight being lifted. Such forces sometimes tear out tendons or seriously injure muscles.

In performing the powerlifts, the danger comes from another source. It comes from prolonged exposure to a force that may be more than the skeleton is capable of supporting, regardless of the strength of the muscles involved. Today, at least a few individuals are squatting with over 900 pounds—and since most of these men weigh at least 300 pounds, this means they are actually supporting over 1,200 pounds on their feet and most of that amount on their spines. The human skeleton was not designed to support such loads for prolonged periods of time. For any purpose except powerlifting competition, all the benefits that can be provided by squats can be derived without using more than 400 pounds, and in most cases without using more than 300 pounds.

HIGH REPETITIONS

There is no question about the effectiveness of squats. They are one of the most result-producing of all exercises. But it is not necessary to do heavy, single-attempt squats to derive benefits. On the contrary, the most result-producing version of squats is to do sets of from fifteen to twenty repetitions.

If two sets of squats are practiced three times weekly, and if a weight is used that will barely permit the performance of between fifteen and twenty repetitions, then this work will stimulate enormous overall growth. Such exercise will also increase endurance, improve condition, and build great strength in both the legs and lower back, as well as build general strength throughout the body.

DEPTH OF SQUATTING

As mentioned earlier, squats should be carried to the point where the thighs first start to contact the backs of the calves. At that point the squat should be stopped by muscular action instead of by bouncing the thighs off the calves. Performed in the correct manner, there is no danger to the knees. On the contrary, squats can do more to prevent knee injuries than any other barbell exercise.

The greatest single disadvantage squats have is that they are brutally hard. Many bodybuilders are simply not willing to work as hard as squats force them to work. Such people have been quick to spread the rumors about the supposed danger to the knees from squats. It is this supposed danger that gives them their excuse for not performing squats.

Joints are not damaged by normal movements. In fact, such movements are required to maintain the normal functioning of joints. Held in one position for several days, a joint becomes temporarily incapable of movement. Held in one position for a few months, a joint may well become permanently incapable of movement.

While squatting as a form of sitting is not customary in this country, it still remains worldwide the most common means of sitting. Furthermore, empirical evidence shows that knee injuries are far more common in this country, where squatting is almost never practiced, than they are in countries where squatting is done routinely.

SQUATS FOR OVERALL SIZE AND STRENGTH

By all means, include squats in your bodybuilding program, and carry them to the lowest safe position. Do them smoothly and under full control at all times. Keep your head up at all times, and do not bounce at the bottom.

Use squats to your advantage, and all your routines will be more productive. They are a key factor in building overall muscular size and strength.

Extremely heavy weights are not necessary to get maximum results from multiple-joint exercises, such as the bench press, squat, and deadlift. Tremendous benefits can be derived from using fairly high repetitions with no more than 300 pounds.

At a special corner of Gold's Gym in Venice, California, four trainees sit awaiting their turn at the squat racks.

Chapter 8

Irregularity of Training

For bodybuilding, if weeks didn't exist, then it might have been necessary to invent them. Evidence shows that a seven-day cycle of training is almost perfect for the production of best results from exercise. This is primarily true, it seems, because it provides needed irregularity of training.

VARIETY IN TRAINING

The human body quickly grows accustomed to almost any activity. Once having adapted to an activity, then no amount of practice of the same activity will provide growth stimulation. It is important to provide as many forms of variation in training as are reasonably possible. In practice, this does not mean that the training program needs to

(*Left*) The sharp muscularity of Bertil Fox's upper body is evident in this pose.
(*Above*) The amazing body of Kay Baxter.

or should be changed frequently. On the contrary, the same basic training routine will serve a bodybuilder well for his entire active life.

A paradox? No, only an apparent one. In the first place, the double progressive system of exercise provides a great deal of variation in training. Secondly, the three-times-weekly training schedule provides even more variety. Finally, if the training program is varied one day weekly, then all the variety that is needed is well provided for.

In the double progressive system of training—and this is the basic principle behind all forms of worthwhile exercise—no two workouts should ever be exactly the same. The system works as follows: A weight is selected that will permit the performance of a certain number of repetitions—but then all possible repetitions are performed with that same resistance, with a constant attempt to increase the

Both female and male bodybuilders should adhere to the same basic principles of training. Here, Kay Baxter displays a highly developed upper body.

THREE TIMES WEEKLY

Even more variety of training is provided by the three-times-weekly schedule. A first workout is performed on Monday, a second on Wednesday, and a third on Friday. On Sunday the body is expecting and is prepared for a fourth workout, but it doesn't come. Instead, it comes a day later, on Monday of the next week when the body is neither expecting nor prepared for it. This schedule of training prevents the body from falling into a rut, since the system is never quite able to adjust to this irregularity of training. Growth stimulation will be produced as a direct result.

If the training program itself is varied insofar as the number of sets and/or the number of repetitions are concerned during one of the three weekly workouts, all the necessary variety and irregularity of training will be produced.

WASTED EFFORT

Many thousands of bodybuilders practice six or seven weekly workouts. In almost all cases, such workouts quickly degenerate into a form of rather hard manual labor. Although some results are produced, they do not measure up to those obtained from a properly designed and executed training program. It takes such trainees four or five years to attain exactly the same results that could have been produced by less than a full year of proper training.

A properly planned and executed training program is nothing short of brutally hard work. Results come almost in direct proportion to the actual intensity of effort above a certain point, and no results are obtained by any amount of work below a certain intensity of effort. Most trainees are simply not willing to work as hard as is required for best results.

WHEN TO CHEAT

Where possible, it is usually desirable to inspire a sense of competition. In practice, however, this frequently leads to poor training habits. Emphasis should be placed on form, and no credit should be permitted for the employment of cheating methods. While cheating methods should be used, they should be employed only at the end of a set of exercise movements that have been performed in perfect form. At that point, cheating makes it possible to induce even more growth stimulation than would otherwise have been possible. If cheating methods are utilized to the exclusion of movements performed in good form, then very little in the way of growth stimulation will be induced. Furthermore, it will then become impossible to measure the progress of individual trainees with anything approaching accuracy.

It is essential to observe carefully the progress of all types of physical training. The requirements for exercise vary to a degree among any group of individuals, although nowhere close to the degree that many people believe. Increasing the workload may produce striking results in some individuals, either increasing the rate of growth enormously or stopping it cold in its tracks. Such results can be produced by a variation of less than 50 percent in the workload. Careful attention must be paid to the true rate of progress of all trainees. This is only possible when performances are measured on a realistic basis, which is simply impossible if cheating methods are permitted during regular workouts and used as the basis for computing rates of progress.

So, practice cheating methods, but only after all possible movements have been performed in good form. Then record only the properly performed movements.

Chapter 9

Inducing Growth Stimulation

(*Left and Page 73 Top*) An assistant gives Greg DeFerro just enough help to get him past the sticking point of his biceps exercise. (*Page 73 Bottom*) Now Greg prepares for another repetition.

aximum growth stimulation can and should be induced by the minimum amount of exercise—the minimum amount required to obtain the desired effects. Once these effects are produced, then additional amounts of exercise will actually reduce the production of increases in strength and muscular size.

At the start of a barbell curl, for example, the arms are straight and the bending muscles of the arms are in stretched positions. In that position the strength of the muscles involved in performing a curl is low. The individual muscle fibers are stretched, and the muscles as a whole are also extended. Secondly, in that position it is impossible to involve more than a low percentage of the total number of available muscle fibers in the action of starting the curl.

The intensity of effort is evident on Casey Viator's face as he performs dumbbell curls.

Muscle fibers perform work by contracting, which reduces their length. To contract, they must move. While it is true that a certain amount of slack exists in muscular structures, it is also true that no significant amount of power can be produced by a muscle without movement. Thus, in effect, as a muscle fiber performs work it contracts, and in so doing it exerts a pulling force and movement of the relaxed body part. Without such movement, no significant amount of power results.

If all the fibers in a particular muscle were contracted at the same time, then the muscle as a whole would be reduced to its shortest length. This cannot happen unless the related body part is moved into its position of full contraction as well. If a muscle did contract fully, and if the related body part did not move into its position of full contraction, then the muscle would be torn loose from its attachments.

Thus, it is impossible to involve all the fibers of the bending muscles of the arms in the performance of curls in any position except a position of full-body-part flexion. In the case of the curl, this means that the arms must be fully bent, fully supinated, and slightly raised.

With a barbell, it is impossible to perform a curl in such a manner that all the muscular fibers of the bending muscles will be involved in the exercise. If all the related factors are understood, and if exercises are performed in a proper manner, then you can at least involve a far higher percentage of the total number of available fibers than you would otherwise.

THE FIRST REPETITION

At the start of the first repetition of a set of ten repetitions of the barbell curl, your muscles are fresh and strong. In that starting position, however, you can involve only a few of the actual number of fibers. This happens because most of the fibers cannot perform work in that position. Only the actual number of fibers required will be involved because individual muscle fibers perform on an all-or-nothing basis.

You could increase the percentage of fibers involved by performing the movement as fast as possible. This is not desirable because fast movements performed when the muscles are fresh are dangerous; there is greater danger of tearing the muscle attachments loose. Furthermore, with fast movements there is always a tendency to swing the weight by overall body motion rather than moving it by action of the muscles you are attempting to exercise.

So the first repetition should be performed slowly and smoothly in perfect form. If any doubt regarding form exists, then the first several repetitions should be done more slowly, to assure that perfect form is maintained.

But in any case, regardless of how you perform the first repetition, you will be involving only a very small percentage of the total number of muscle fibers available. At the start of the first repetition, it is impossible to involve more than very few of the total number of fibers because most of the fibers cannot work in that position. At the top of the exercise where it is possible to involve a higher percentage of the total number of available fibers, there is little resistance available.

If you are using a weight with which you can perform ten repetitions of the barbell curl, a properly performed first repetition may involve only 4 or 5 percent of the total number of available fibers. The other 90-odd percent of available fibers are in no way involved in the exercise.

ADDITIONAL REPETITIONS

During an immediately following second repetition, the previously worked fibers are no longer as fresh and strong as they were during the first repetition. Their strength level has been reduced, and they will not again be capable of raising the weight without the assistance of other fibers. Such assistance will be provided again, but only to the degree actually required.

Thus, repetition by repetition the percentage of involved fibers becomes greater, until, by the tenth repetition, you may be using as many as 15 percent of the total number of available fibers. At that time the exercise will seem quite hard, and most trainees will call a halt to their efforts.

But at that point in the exercise, little muscle-growth stimulation has been induced. The muscles are already capable of performing at the level being demanded—as was demonstrated by the fact that you could perform ten repetitions. And thus, the muscles are not being forced to work inside their momentarily existing levels of reserve strength. In effect, the muscles can perform the work being demanded of them, and they can do so without exhausting their reserves. Therefore there is no need for them to grow.

But if instead of stopping at the tenth repetition you had continued with the exercise, forcing the muscles to work much harder than normal and requiring them to work well inside their reserves of strength, then muscle-growth stimulation would have resulted.

MAXIMUM REPETITIONS

How many more repetitions should be done?

As many as possible, regardless of the actual number this may prove to be. The set should be terminated only when it is impossible to move the weight in any position, when the bar literally drops out of your exhausted hands.

Even then, with a barbell you still won't be involving all of the available fibers. You will, at least, be involving as high a percentage as possible with conventional forms of exercise. And you will be inducing as much muscle-growth stimulation as possible with a barbell or any other type of conventional training equipment.

If you are training in that manner, then only one such set is required—three times weekly—in most cases, and never more than two such sets in any case. Doing a larger number of lighter sets will not produce the same results. Doing a larger number of properly performed sets would exhaust your recovery ability so much that losses would be produced instead of gains.

Watching a man working out properly is frightening. The intensity of effort is so great that his entire body is shaking, his face will turn dark red, and his breathing and heart action will be increased at least 100 percent.

Most people are simply not aware that such effort is even possible, and many who are aware of the possibility are totally unwilling to exert such effort. For maximum growth stimulation, however, that is exactly what is required. Left alone, most trainees will make little progress because they won't work hard enough to induce growth stimulation. For best results, all your workouts should be carefully supervised.

Chapter 10

For many champions, successful training involves as many psychological as physiological variables.

Secondary Growth Factors

(*Top Left*) A balanced diet for bodybuilding should be composed of 55 percent carbohydrates, 30 percent fats, and 15 percent proteins. Here, Reid Shindle enjoys a meal. (*Top Right*) Sergio Oliva is preparing a crab leg for tasty consumption. (*Bottom*) You can have your cake and eat it too! Greg DeFerro is a believer in a high-carbohydrate diet. Here he enjoys a piece of strawberry cream cake.

egardless of how much growth stimulation is induced, results will be poor unless the requirements of several other factors are also provided. Basically, these are as follows: (1) nutrition, (2) adequate rest, (3) avoidance of overwork, and (4) various psychological variables.

NUTRITION

Nothing bordering on any form of fanaticism in nutrition is required for building muscle. Yet such fanaticism exists on a wide scale in bodybuilding today. Much of such fanaticism is a result of commercialized fraud, perpetrated for the purpose of selling useless products for financial gain.

Bodybuilders should not let themselves become dehydrated. It is important to drink plenty of fluids before, during, and after your training sessions.

...s of trainees are existing on diets of nearly pure protein, others consume hundreds of ... day, and quite a number are taking various forms of so-called "growth drugs." None of ... ..e justified. Maximum possible gains from any training program can be produced while ...ormal life. In fact, there is much evidence supporting the contention that a normal existence is ...ily a requirement for maximum gains.

An individual on a program of heavy exercise naturally requires enough calories to suppy the energy needed for such training if he hopes to maintain his existing bodyweight. To gain bodyweight requires even more in the way of nutritional factors. But such requirements can and should come from a normal balanced diet.

A balanced diet is composed of approximately 55 percent carbohydrates, 30 percent fats, and 15 percent proteins. This can be supplied easily by several servings a day from the Basic Four Food Groups: meats, dairy products, fruits and vegetables, and breads and cereals. Nothing else in the way of a special diet is required.

There is little evidence to support the need for supplementary vitamins if a well-balanced diet is provided. Indeed, the available evidence clearly indicates that such vitamin intake is of no value.

Where additional calories are required—in the case of a bodybuilder who wishes to gain weight rapidly as a result of his training—they can be obtained from commonly available sources: eggs, powdered milk, bananas, and frozen orange juice concentrate. Two or three daily blender drinks made according to the following recipe will provide more than enough calories for an average man anxious to gain weight rapidly, if taken in addition to his normal meals.

Special Drink

1 egg	½ banana
⅓ cup frozen orange juice concentrate	¾ cup whole milk
¼ cup powdered milk	4 ice cubes

Place all ingredients in a blender and mix for thirty seconds. Pour into a large glass and drink.

Consume three of these special drinks daily: one at midmorning, a second immediately after work or school, and a third just before retiring for the night.

For a complete discussion of food, nutrition, and athletic performance, please see *The Nautilus Nutrition Book*. Information on this book can be obtained by writing to Darden Research Corporation, P.O. Box 1016, Lake Helen, FL 32744.

ADEQUATE REST AND OVERWORK

The requirements for adequate rest are no more complicated than those dictated by common sense and good health habits. Some people require more sleep than others, so get as much as is normal for you as an individual. Your results will be less if you make a common practice of getting too little rest, but excessive amounts of sleep will probably retard your progress also. Simply continue with your normally practiced good habits in regard to sleep.

Other activities should continue as before. Better progress will almost always be shown by an individual who is regularly employed in some full-time activity, such as a normal job or a normal load of schoolwork. Too many bodybuilders believe that activities should be strictly limited to workouts, eating, and sleeping.

Where other sports activities are concerned, their effect on training progress can be either good or bad. It will be almost impossible for a man to gain muscle mass rapidly if he makes a daily practice of running several miles. But if such running is a necessary part of his sports training, then it naturally should be done. The same rule is equally applicable to any other activity: Do what is necessary, and the weight-training program will markedly increase your strength and improve your overall condition, even if it does not result in great increases in muscular size under such conditions.

People who are overly fat should engage in extra activities until the surplus fat is lost. Overfat people almost never have much endurance or energy level at the start of such a program. Great care

The symmetrical posing team of Gladys Portugues and Tom Terwilliger.

must be taken to prevent them from working to the point of nervous exhaustion. Removing the last traces of fatty tissue almost always involves overwork.

The arms, shoulders, chest, and legs should show a high degree of muscularity, but a small amount of fatty tissue should remain in the area of the waist and the buttocks.

If such a condition does not exist to at least a reasonable degree, and if an extreme degree of muscularity is evident over the entire body, then it is probable that the individual is overworked. His workouts should be reduced until his bodyweight is increasing.

PSYCHOLOGICAL FACTORS

Psychological factors required for the best bodybuilding results are indeed important. Some of the more important factors are visualization, mirrors, before-and-after photographs, and progress charts.

Visualization is picturing in your mind the bodybuilding results you would like to achieve. These images help you to focus your energies on accomplishing your goals.

Be positive, but at the same time be realistic in your expectations. For example, picture yourself with a deeper chest and larger, more defined arms. Establish step-by-step goals in your mind. Visualize your arms growing by ½ inch, then 1 inch, and finally 1½ inches. Increase your expectations gradually and you'll be more successful.

A large mirror placed appropriately in your training area assists you in three ways. First, looking at your body in a mirror helps you to visualize your training goals. Second, performing most of the recommended exercises in front of a mirror allows you to isolate the involved muscles more completely. Third, training in front of a mirror is motivating because you actually see your muscles expand as they contract.

Photographs also can provide valuable feedback and important motivation. Have a friend take some photographs of you in a snug bathing suit from the front, back, and side. First, stand relaxed against an uncluttered background. Then try a double-armed, contracted biceps pose from the front and back.

Take your measurements at the same time and note the date. Get the film developed and file the photographs and measurements for safekeeping.

Repeat the picture-taking sessions every month. Compare the photographs with the preceding sets. Such comparisons will help you evaluate the results of your bodybuilding program.

The last psychological factor concerns your progress chart. It is important that you keep accurate records of all your workouts. This is usually done on a card that lists the exercises with ample space to the right for recording the date, order, resistance, and repetitions.

(*Opposite: Top Left*) Jesup Wilkosz's extreme muscularity is a result of his low level of subcutaneous fat. (*Top Right*) Visualization plays an important role in the development of Albert Beckles's mighty biceps. (*Bottom*) High-intensity training stimulates your muscles to grow. But the actual growth occurs during the following 48 hours. That is why it is important to get adequate rest after your workouts.

Chapter 11

The Recovery Factor

**hen** a muscle has been worked to a point of momentary failure by heavy exercise, the situation is just that—the muscle has failed momentarily. But in most cases, within 3 seconds the muscle has recovered approximately 50 percent of the strength it had lost as a result of the exercise. But it does not follow that it will then be fully recovered in 6 seconds or even 6 minutes. Full recovery usually takes more than 24 hours and frequently as much as 40 to 60 hours. But even if the muscle itself does recover entirely, this is no indication that the system supplying the muscle is fully recovered.

To produce increases in size and strength, the muscles must be induced to make certain (but largely unknown) demands on the system as a

(*Left*) Albert Beckles realizes that rest and recovery are as important to the muscle-building program as high-intensity exercise. (*Above*) Tina Plakinger and Mary Roberts compare back poses at the 1984 Professional Women's Bodybuilding Championships in Toronto.

Carla Dunlap and Tony Pearson, winners of the 1984 Professional Mixed Pairs Championships in Toronto, Canada.

Bob Birdsong and Mary Roberts, runners-up in the same contest.

whole for the materials required for growth. But growth cannot result even then if the system is unable to supply the needed materials. This is not simply a matter of assuring that the right food has been eaten. The primary limiting factor in this case is the ability of the system to make the required physiological changes within the allotted period of time. If another workout occurs before these processes are complete, then little in the way of growth can occur.

In practice, it takes hard work to induce growth—and time to permit growth.

There will be individual variation, of course, but only within a rather limited scale. It is also true that the recovery ability of a well-trained individual will be better than it was before he started training, but again, only to a certain degree. Please note the wording "well-trained," not "long-trained." In fact, many advanced bodybuilders have very poor recovery abilities because they have overworked their systems for months or years.

A LIMITED SUPPLY

An in-depth discussion of recovery ability is beyond the scope of this book. Furthermore, it is not really necessary. What is necessary is an awareness of the existence of a limited recovery ability and an application of this awareness.

When anything is in limited supply, then it is simply common sense to make the best utilization of the quantity that is available. When you are not sure how much is available, it is equally good practice to use as little as necessary. In bodybuilding the implication is clear: Use your limited recovery ability as wisely as possible and as little as possible in line with the actual requirements for producing the results you are after.

It really doesn't matter "why" high-intensity exertion is required to induce muscular growth or exactly "how" this is brought about. It is equally unimportant for us to understand the actual reasons for the limitations in our recovery ability. But it is necessary to know that hard work is required, and that recovery ability is limited. A failure to understand these factors has led to the presently existing situation in bodybuilding, with almost all trainees working far too much and very few trainees working hard enough. Rather than constantly trying to increase the length of workouts, all trainees would be well advised to reduce their training to an absolute minimum.

CYCLE TRAINING

Part of this requirement for reduced weekly training time will be produced by cycle training. It should be understood that we are not using cycle training merely in an attempt to save training time; we are using it because it is a requirement for producing maximum results. To work a particular muscle as hard as it must be worked to induce maximum growth stimulation, while staying within the limits imposed by the overall recovery ability of the system, you must use cycle training. When this is done properly, then only one or two brief cycles are all that are required. Doing more cycles may or may not induce more growth stimulation, but even if it did, growth would be impossible in many cases and very slow in all cases.

For example, we have produced good results from the following training schedule for the arms:
1. One set of twelve repetitions, standing barbell curls
   Rush!
2. One set of regular grip chin-ups, maximum repetitions
3. One set of twelve repetitions, standing triceps extensions with a heavy dumbbell held lengthways between both hands
   Rush!
4. One set of dips, maximum repetitions
5. One set of fifteen repetitions, wrist curls with a barbell
6. One set of fifteen repetitions, reverse wrist curls with a barbell

The triceps extension is a single-joint exercise that isolates the triceps.
Parallel dips are a multiple-joint exercise that brings into action the deltoids and pectorals to force the triceps to a deeper level of stimulation.

THE RUSH FACTOR

The rush factor occurs twice during the schedule: between the first and second sets, and between the third and fourth sets. At those points in the workout you must move from the end of one set to the start of the next set as quickly as possible—and certainly in less than three seconds.

Properly performed, this schedule requires a total of five minutes and twenty seconds—or exactly sixteen minutes weekly, since some of our trainees use it three times weekly.

Please note, the above schedule is not intended only for beginners. It has been used by some of the strongest men in the world. At times they do a bit more, but at other times they do quite a bit less.

When any doubt exists, always do less. Never do much more.

Training schedules for other muscular structures of the body are for the most part even briefer, and they usually involve the rush factor between all sets within the cycles being used. The rush factor—movement from the end of one set to the start of the next set with almost zero delay—makes it possible to work a muscle far beyond its normal point of failure. In the arm routine just outlined, for example, it works as follows: The third set works the triceps to a point of normal failure, thus pre-exhausting the triceps muscles for the work to follow immediately. Then the parallel dips force the triceps to become involved in work that is actually beyond the normal point of failure.

It might appear that a similar result could be produced in another obvious way, by gradually reducing the resistance on the triceps extension so the muscle can work until simply unable to continue even with no resistance. In practice this does not produce results on the same order, for at least two reasons: The repetitions become far too high, and the lack of change of exercises does not provide the needed variety of work. Moving from the triceps extension, which provides work for the primary function of the triceps muscles, to the parallel dips, which provide work in the position of contraction for the secondary function of the triceps, makes it possible to work much more of the actual mass of the triceps muscles while still not moving outside the limits of the recovery ability.

A very similar principle is involved in the work for the biceps when you move immediately from curls to chin-ups.

No amount of exercises performed in any other fashion will produce equal results. Increasing the amount of exercise almost always reduces the production of results, even when similar principles are employed—and especially so, in fact. This is hard exercise. You don't need much of it. Truth is, you can't tolerate much.

Franco Columbu on the night he won the 1981 Mr. Olympia.
(*Overleaf*) It takes high-intensity exercise to induce muscular growth—
and time to permit growth. Bertil Fox understands the proper balance between work and rest.

Chapter 12

Other Training Considerations

his chapter discusses the correct duration, frequency, and order of your high-intensity workouts.

DURATION OF WORKOUTS

The effect of high-intensity exercise on the entire body can be either good or bad. If high-intensity work is followed by an adequate period of rest, then muscular growth and an increase in strength will occur.

High-intensity work is required for growth stimulation, but it must not be overdone.

Many bodybuilders make the mistake of performing far too much exercise: too

(*Left*) Lou Ferrigno flexes his mighty arms before a workout.
(*Above*) Leaning forward curls involve the biceps more in the contracted position.

many different exercises, too many sets, and too many workouts within a given period of time. When an excessive amount of exercise is performed, total recovery between workouts becomes impossible, and high-intensity training then becomes equally impossible.

You can have one or the other, but not both. You can perform high-intensity exercise on a brief and infrequent basis with good results. Or you can perform long and frequent low-intensity workouts with very poor results. But you cannot perform long and frequent workouts involving intense work. Attempting to do so will produce losses in both muscular mass and strength. In addition, it may result in total collapse.

In most cases, not more than a combined total of twenty sets of different exercises should be performed in any one training session. (*Note:* This does not mean twenty sets of each exercise; it

To be effective, high-intensity exercise must be brief and infrequent.

means twenty overall sets per workout.) If you are pushed to an all-out effort in each of the twenty sets, you will not want to do more overall exercise. In fact, your body will not be able to stand more.

A high-intensity set, performed properly, takes about 1 minute to complete. Allowing about 1 minute between exercises means that most bodybuilders should be able to complete twenty exercises or sets in under 40 minutes. Actually, as bodybuilders work themselves into better shape, the time between exercises should be reduced.

Most of your bodybuilding workouts should be 40 minutes or less in duration. Thus, your total weekly training time should be limited to 2 hours.

FREQUENCY OF WORKOUTS

Research has shown that there should be approximately 48 hours between high-intensity workouts. In some cases, where extremely strong athletes are training, 72 hours are required. On the other hand, high levels of muscular size and strength start to decrease after 96 hours of normal activity.

An every-other-day training schedule—Monday, Wednesday, and Friday, or Tuesday, Thursday, and Saturday—is ideally suited for most bodybuilders.

Many authorities have noted that high-intensity exercise for the major muscle masses results in large-scale growth for those muscles as well as lower order of growth in other muscles. Arthur Jones believes that this "indirect growth effect" occurs as a result of a chemical reaction. As a muscle works intensively, a chemical reaction occurs that spills over and affects the entire body.

Since there is a limit to your overall recovery ability, and since many of the body's chemical functions affect the entire body, it should be evident that training every day is a mistake. Even if a split routine—a training program that works the lower body one day and the upper body the next day—is used, the system cannot recover from a hard workout in fewer than 48 hours. If a high-intensity lower body workout is done between each hard workout for the upper body, the overall system will never be given enough time for full recovery and growth. Even though the bodybuilder who uses a split routine believes he is only working the upper or lower body, this is impossible because of the indirect growth effect.

Rather than using the indirect growth effect to your disadvantage, use it to your advantage. Instead of training every day on a split routine, train your body in an overall fashion only three times a week.

ORDER OF EXERCISES

Young bodybuilders tend to ignore the development of their legs, concentrating instead on their arms and torso. Such a lopsided program will permit the arms to grow up to a point. Additional growth will not take place, however, until heavy exercises for the legs are added. Then the arms immediately start growing.

While the amount of growth resulting from this factor is not known, it is apparent that it varies within a certain range. Such variation seems to depend on two conditions: (1) the larger the muscle mass exercised, the larger the indirect growth effect will be and (2) the greater the distance between the muscle being exercised and the muscle not being exercised, the smaller the indirect growth effect will be.

Thus, it is clear that working only the arms would have the largest indirect effect on nearby muscular masses such as the deltoids, pectorals, latissimus, and trapezius. And this work would have the least effect on the gastrocnemius muscles of the lower legs. It is also clear that the indirect effect produced by building the arms would not be as great as that resulting from exercising the much larger muscles of the thighs or upper back.

From these observations, several important conclusions can be drawn:

1. For maximum bodybuilding, the training program must be well-rounded and must include exercises for each of the major muscle masses.

2. The greatest concentration should be directed toward working the largest muscles in the body.

3. The exercise sequence should be arranged so the muscles are worked in the order of their relative sizes, from largest to smallest.

In practice, this last point prescribes that the lower body be worked before the upper body. As a rule, your thighs are exercised before the calves, the back before the chest, and the upper arms before the forearms.

Since the waist muscles are used to stabilize the upper body in most exercises, they should be worked after the arms and forearms. The muscles of the neck, because of their critical location, should be exercised last.

THE MECHANICS OF MUSCULAR GROWTH

Muscular growth is a result of what physiologists call overcompensation. The formation of a callus is often cited as an example of this overcompensation process.

The skin on your palms is naturally thicker than it is on the backs of your hands. This extra thickness will be found on the palms even if you have never done manual labor. But if you perform hard work with your hands, work that brings your hands in contact with abrasive objects, the thickness of the skin on your palms may not be sufficient to protect you. In this case you will develop a callus in any area exposed to such work, *as long as the conditions are right*.

For the conditions to be right, the work must be hard enough to stimulate the growth of a callus. But the work must not reach an amount that will *prevent* the growth of a callus. If you work hard, the growth of a callus will be stimulated. If you work too much, the growth will not take place.

No amount of gentle rubbing on the palm of your hand will stimulate the growth of a callus. It is not the amount of contact that causes a callus to grow. Instead, if you rub your hand only a few times, but hard, the growth of a callus will be stimulated.

If you rub your hand too many times, or too often, however, no callus will result. The body may be trying to form a callus, but the rubbing will remove the growing tissue faster than the body can provide it.

Muscular growth takes place in a similar fashion for similar reasons. Part of such growth is natural. But beyond a certain point muscular growth must be stimulated. Such extra growth will not occur unless it is stimulated by heavy demands on the existing levels of muscular size. And it cannot occur unless the recovery ability of the system is able to compensate and overcompensate at the same time.

If all the recovery ability of the system is used up in efforts to compensate, no energy will be left for the overcompensation that produces greater-than-normal growth.

In practice, most bodybuilders fall into a pattern in which the amount of their training uses up all of their recovery ability. Growth thus becomes impossible. They seldom train hard enough to stimulate overcompensation, so little or no growth can occur even though their system is capable of overcompensation.

Don't let your training fall into this category. Stimulate your muscles to grow by training harder. Then allow your stimulated muscles to grow by keeping your workouts brief and infrequent.

Chapter 13

The stiff-legged deadlift is one of the best barbell exercises for building overall size and strength. Performed properly, it also makes heavy demands on your recovery ability.

High-Intensity Guidelines

ere are the high-intensity guidelines summarized from the previous chapters.

1. Perform no more than a total of twenty sets of all exercises in any one training session.

2. Train no more than three times a week. Each workout should involve the entire body, as opposed to splitting the routine into lower and upper body work on separate days.

3. Select resistance for each exercise that allows the performance of between eight and twelve repetitions. Higher repetitions, from fifteen to twenty, may be used for the lower body.

4. Continue each exercise until momentary muscular failure. When more than the guide number of repetitions are performed, increase the resistance by approximately 5 percent at the next workout.

5. Work your largest muscles first and your smallest muscles last.

6. Accentuate the negative or lowering portion of each repetition. Lift the weight in two seconds and lower it in four seconds.

7. Move slower, never faster, if in doubt about the speed of movement.

8. Attempt constantly to increase the number of repetitions or the amount of weight, or both. But do not sacrifice form in an attempt to increase the repetitions or weight.

9. Get ample rest after each training session. High-intensity exercise necessitates a recovery period of at least 48 hours. Muscles grow during rest, not during exercise.

10. Eat a balanced diet composed of several servings a day from the Basic Four Food Groups. Protein supplements and vitamin–mineral pills are not necessary.

11. Train with a partner who can reinforce proper form on each exercise.

12. Keep accurate records—date, order, resistance, repetitions, and overall training time—of each workout.

(*Opposite Page Left*) A twisting back pose of Lee Haney. (*Opposite Page Right*) Johnny Fuller displays unusual thickness throughout his entire back. (*Above*) Work your biceps toward the end of your routine. (*Inset*) The largest muscles of the back, the latissimus dorsi muscles, require at least 40 hours of recovery after they are worked intensely.

Part II

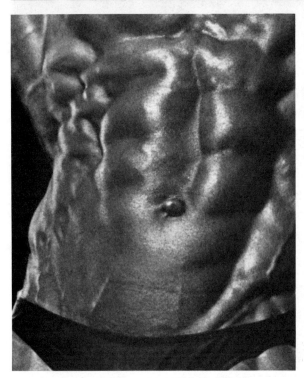

High-Intensity Routines

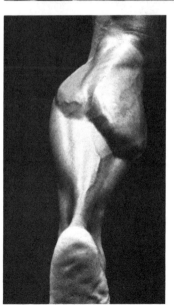

Chapter 14

Building Overall Size and Strength

n simple terms, it takes muscle to lift weights. The more muscle a person has, the more weight he can lift. Adding muscle size will always make a man stronger. Increasing his strength will always increase his muscle size.

The facts are clear. If you are interested in developing the size of your muscles, then you must train for maximum muscular strength to build maximum muscular size.

Let's assume, for example, that you are between 18 and 25 years of age, weigh approximately 150 pounds, have never weight trained consistently, and are in normal health. Your goal is to get as big and strong as possible by increasing the size and strength of your major muscles.

Available training equipment includes barbells, dumbbells, a squat rack, a bench with

(*Left*) Sergio Oliva, at 5 feet, 10 inches and 233 pounds, represents the ultimate in overall muscular size and strength.
(*Above Left*) Lance Dreher shows an excellent combination of mass and muscularity.
(*Above Right*) Progressive exercise is the secret to the massive muscles of Bertil Fox.

...cks, a chinning bar, a set of parallel bars, a conventional leg extension machine, and a ...onal leg curl machine.

...SIC HIGH-INTENSITY ROUTINE

Your basic routine for building overall size and strength is as follows:

Exercise	Guideline for Repetitions
1. Full squat	20
2. Straight-armed pullover with one dumbbell while lying crossways on a bench	12
3. Full squat	20
4. Straight-armed pullover with one dumbbell	12
5. Leg extension	12
6. Leg curl	12
7. One-legged calf raise	15
8. One-legged calf raise	15
9. Press behind neck	12
10. Behind neck chin-up	12
11. Bench press	12
12. Bent-over row	12
13. Parallel dip	12
14. Biceps curl	12
15. Triceps extension with one dumbbell held in both hands	12
16. Regular chin-up	12
17. Parallel dip	12
18. Stiff-legged deadlift	15
19. Wrist curl	12
20. Trunk curl	12

This listing and sequence of exercises has been tried and proved effective. Keeping the high-intensity guidelines from Chapter 13 in mind, you should perform each exercise in the following manner.

Full squat: The barbell should be in the top position of the squat racks. Step under the barbell and place the barbell behind your neck and across your shoulders. Stand erect and step back. Your feet should be approximately shoulder-width apart, and your head should be kept up at all times. Bend your knees and hips, and lower your buttocks slowly into a full squat. Do not bounce in and out of the bottom position. Return to the standing position in a smooth fashion. Take a deep breath, and repeat for twenty repetitions.

Straight-armed pullover with one dumbbell while lying crossways on a bench: Assume a supine position crossways on a bench with your shoulders in contact with the bench and your head and lower body relaxed and off the bench. A dumbbell, held on one end, is positioned over your chest in a straight-armed manner. Take a deep breath and lower the dumbbell behind your head. Stretch and return the dumbbell to the over-chest position. It is important to keep your arms straight during the movement and to emphasize the stretching of the torso when the dumbbell is behind your head. Repeat for twelve repetitions.

Rest briefly, and then perform a second set of squats and a second set of pullovers.

Leg extension: This is the best exercise for your quadriceps or frontal thigh muscles. Sit in the machine and place your feet behind the roller pads. If possible, align the axis of rotation of the machine with your knees. Lean back and stabilize your body by grasping the sides of the machine. Straighten your legs smoothly. Pause at the point of full muscular contraction. Do not bounce in and out of the position. Lower slowly and repeat.

Leg curl: This is the most productive movement for your hamstrings. Lie face down on the machine and place your heels under the roller pads. Make certain that your knees are in line with the axis of rotation of the machine. Bend your legs and try to touch your heels to your buttocks. In the fully contracted position, your buttocks should be raised, and you should come to a complete stop. Lower slowly and repeat.

One-legged calf raise: A sturdy, four-inch step is necessary to perform this exercise. In a standing position with a dumbbell in the right hand, place the ball of the right foot on the block. Use your left arm to stabilize your body. While keeping the right knee locked, raise and lower your heel in a smooth, slow manner. When your right calf is exhausted, switch the dumbbell to the left hand and repeat the procedure with your left calf. Perform a second set for your right calf and a second set for your left.

Press behind neck: A barbell is placed behind your neck. You should be standing, with your hands slightly wider than your shoulders. Press the barbell smoothly over your head. Keep your elbows wide as the barbell is slowly returned to the standing position behind your neck. Repeat for twelve repetitions.

Behind neck chin-up: Hang from a horizontal bar with your hands approximately twelve inches wider than your shoulders. Use an overhand grip. Pull your body up and forward until the bar touches behind your neck. Pause at the top. Lower slowly to the bottom position. Repeat.

Bench press: It is best to use a standard bench with support racks for this exercise. Lie on your back and position your body under the racks and the supported barbell. Place your hands shoulder-width apart. Lift the barbell over your chest. Your feet should be flat on the floor in a stable position. Lower the barbell slowly to your chest. Press the barbell smoothly until your arms lock. Repeat.

It is important to perform the bench press without excessive arching of your back. Such arching could be dangerous.

Bent-over row: In a bent-over position, grasp a barbell with shoulder-width grip. Your torso should be parallel with the floor. Pull the barbell upward until it touches your lower chest area. Pause. Return slowly to the stretched position. Repeat.

Parallel dip: This exercise is one of the best, because of its long range of movement, for your chest and upper body. Mount the parallel bars and extend your arms. Bend your arms and lower your body slowly. Stretch at the bottom and smoothly recover to the top position. Repeat.

Biceps curl: The biceps curl may be performed in many ways: the way described here is with a barbell in a standing position. Grasp a barbell with your palms up and your hands about shoulder-width apart. Stand erect. While keeping your body straight, smoothly curl the barbell. Slowly lower, and repeat for eight to twelve repetitions.

Triceps extension with one dumbbell held in both hands: This is the best exercise for isolating the triceps. A dumbbell is held at one end with both hands. Press the dumbbell overhead. Your elbows should be close to your ears. Bend your arms and lower the dumbbell slowly behind your neck. Do not move your elbows; only your forearms and hands should move. Press the dumbbell back to the starting position. Repeat.

Regular chin-up: Grasp the horizontal bar with an underhand grip, and hang. Your hands should be shoulder-width apart. Pull your body upward so your chin is over the bar. In fact, try to touch the bar to your chest. Pause. Lower your body slowly to the hanging position. Repeat.

After the regular chin-ups, perform another set of parallel dips.

Stiff-legged deadlift: This valuable exercise is often neglected by bodybuilders. It strongly involves the lower back, buttocks, and hamstrings. A small platform should be used to increase the range of movement. Stand on the platform and grasp the barbell with an under-and-over grip. Your feet should be under the bar. Lift the barbell to the standing position. With your knees locked, the barbell should be lowered to the stretched position and smoothly lifted back to the top. Repeat for fifteen repetitions.

Wrist curl: Grasp a barbell with a palms-up grip. Rest your forearms on your thighs and the back

(*Top Left*) Leg extension: Pausing when your legs are straight will make this exercise harder. (*Top Right*) Straight-armed pullover: Deep breathing and stretching are the most important factors in performing this exercise.
(*Bottom Left*) Full squat: Keep your head up at all times. (*Bottom Right*) Leg curl: Emphasize the contracted position by moving into it slowly. Do not bounce.

(*Top Left*) One-legged calf raise: Keep your knee locked throughout the entire range of movement. (*Top Right*) Bench press: Do not bounce the bar off your chest. The movement should be slow and smooth. (*Bottom Left*) Press behind neck: Keep your elbows wide and you'll bring into action more of the medial deltoids. (*Bottom Right*) Behind neck chin-up: Minimize your lower body sway by relaxing your abdominals.

(*Top Left*) Bent-over row: Pause when the bar touches your torso. (*Top Right*) Biceps curl: Curl the barbell smoothly and slowly. Do not throw the weight. (*Bottom Left*) Parallel dip: A deep stretch at the bottom makes this exercise more productive. (*Bottom Right*) Triceps extension: Keep your upper arms in a vertical position throughout the movement.

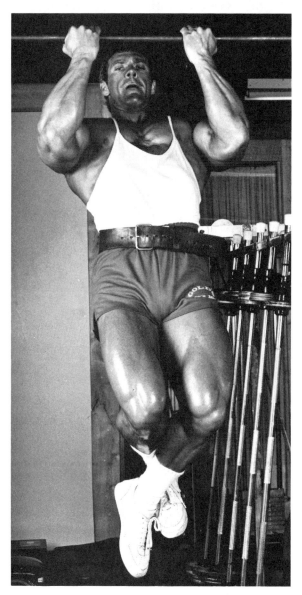

(*Top Left*) Trunk curl: Lift your shoulders and pause in the top position. (*Top Right*) Wrist curl: Do not move your forearms. Only your hands should rotate. (*Bottom Left*) Regular chin-up: Try to increase the range of movement by touching your chest to the bar. (*Bottom Right*) Stiff-legged deadlift: Standing on a bench or on a platform allows a greater range of movement.

of your hands against your knees, and be seated. Lean forward until the angle between your upper arms and forearms is less than 90 degrees. This allows you to isolate the forearms more efficiently. Curl your hands smoothly and contract your forearm muscles. Pause and lower the barbell slowly. Do not allow your forearms or torso to move. Do not extend your fingers. Keep the bar in the palms of your hands. Repeat for twelve repetitions.

Trunk curl: Lie face up on the floor with your hands behind your head. Keep your chin on your chest. Bring your heels up close to your buttocks and spread your knees. Do not anchor your feet under anything. Try to curl your trunk to a sitting position. Only one-third of a standard sit-up can be performed in this fashion. Pause in the contracted position and lower your back slowly to the floor. Repeat for twelve repetitions.

MAXIMIZING RESULTS

The basic routine should be performed three times a week for at least six, or even nine, weeks. But in any case, the program should not be modified until you are capable of performing the following resistance for the required repetitions:

Squat	200/20 (200 pounds for 20 repetitions)
One-legged calf raise	30/15
Press behind neck	120/12
Bench press	140/12
Parallel dip	Bodyweight + 30/12
Chin-up	Bodyweight + 25/12
Biceps curl	100/12
Stiff-legged deadlift	200/15

Some trainees will reach the above levels very quickly, and some will take longer. More specialized training, however, should not be undertaken at strength levels below those listed.

After six to nine weeks of high-intensity training, you should increase your muscle mass by 5 to 10 pounds. You should be more muscular in appearance as well.

There will be a natural temptation to do more, to add sets or new exercises. Faster growth, however, will result if the program is performed exactly as outlined.

At no time should you attempt maximum, single-attempt lifts. Don't worry about what weight you can bench press once, or how much weight you can squat with one time. Maximum attempts are not only dangerous but also an unproductive way to train.

SPECIALIZATION

Sooner or later most bodybuilders have body parts that lag behind, such as the calves, arms, or chest. The next eight chapters present specialized high-intensity routines for major body parts.

Before trying any specialized routine, it is important to remember that your body grows best by working it as an overall unit. If you want a big upper body or big arms specifically, you'll get them faster by working your lower body intensely as well.

Thus, the basic routine presented in this chapter will be referred to throughout the specialized chapters. Even though you may be specializing on a certain muscle group, you'll still be including basic exercises for the other parts of your body. And you'll still be limiting your overall sets per workout to twenty or fewer.

Try to resist the temptation to perform more than two specialized routines during the same workout. For example, you might employ the specialized thigh and arm routine, or calf and shoulder routine, on the same day. Even then, two specialized routines may leave you in a state of overtraining.

The specialized routines for the thighs, calves, chest, shoulders, back, and arms are all designed to shock certain muscle groups into renewed growth. But remember, to become larger and stronger, your muscles must be *permitted* to grow. Make sure your muscles are permitted to grow by not overtraining them. Use the specialized routines wisely and infrequently.

Chapter 15

The unparalleled physique of Sergio Oliva

High-Intensity Thighs

Tom Platz is considered by most authorities to have the greatest hamstrings and quadriceps in bodybuilding.

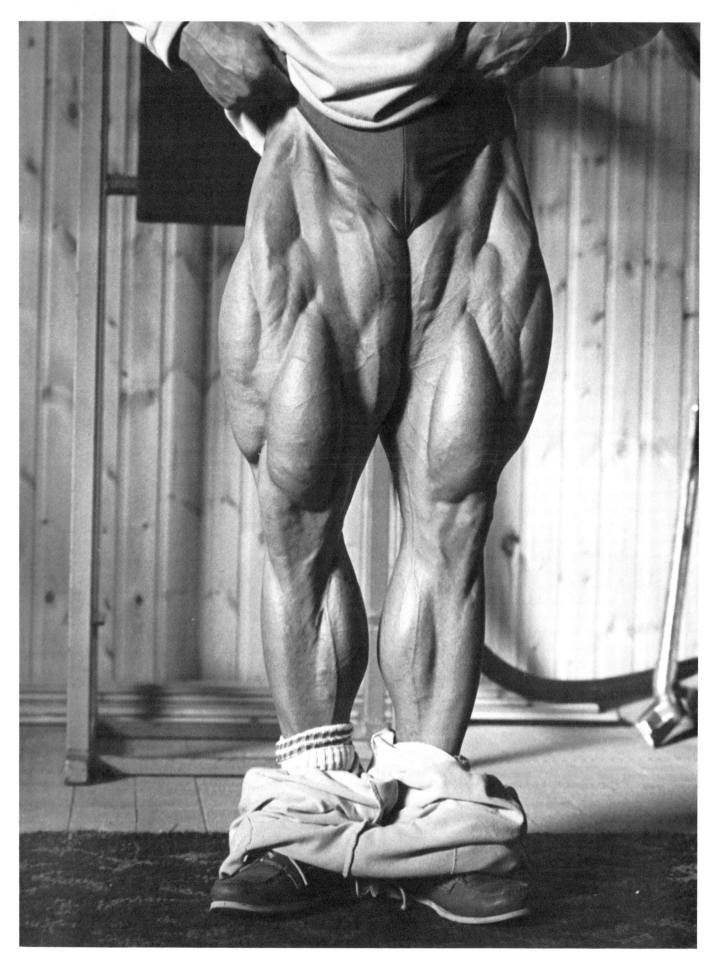

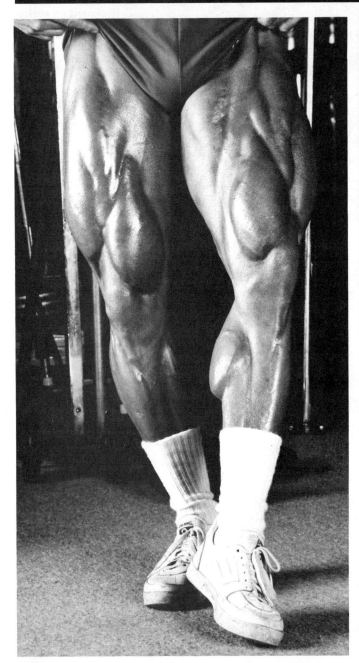

've seen most of the greatest thighs in bodybuilding, such as those of Tom Platz, Mike Mentzer, Casey Viator, Boyer Coe, Chris Dickerson, Jim Haislop, and Lee Haney. One of the greatest pairs of thighs I've ever seen, however, belonged to a man who never won a major physique contest—a man from Tampa, Florida, named Ivor Butcher. What massive and well-defined thighs Butcher had, though he never received the recognition he deserved because his upper body was not up to par with his lower body.

The largest, most impressive thighs I've ever seen belong to a man who is primarily known for his arms and upper body mass, a man who receives little credit for his thighs because his upper body is considered to be the best in the world. The man I'm referring to is Sergio Oliva.

Scott Wilson and Dale Ruplinger have not neglected their quadriceps and hamstrings.

The first time I realized the true size of Sergio's legs was in Daytona Beach, Florida, in August of 1971. Arthur Jones had been personally training Oliva for several weeks as he readied himself to enter the Mr. Universe contest in London, England. I was visiting Jones and had observed him put Sergio through a brief workout for his upper body. During the workout I had been so thoroughly preoccupied with the size of Sergio's arms that I didn't even notice his legs, especially since he was wearing sweatpants.

That night I happened to be on the Boardwalk at Daytona Beach with some friends. We were walking along doing some girl-watchng when all of a sudden Sergio appeared. He was wearing a colorful Japanese kimono with sleeves that covered his arms and a bottom that stopped at his upper thighs.

My first response was, "His thighs must measure at least thirty inches!" They were not only massive but also vascular and cut to ribbons. I would have probably never noticed his legs if he had not had his upper body completely covered with the kimono.

"Dammit Sergio, I never knew you had such fantastic legs," I said as Sergio slowly contracted his huge thighs and smiled as only Sergio can smile.

"Yeah, they've really improved since I've been doing Jones's high-intensity thigh routine," Sergio said with a frown. "And my mother in Cuba hears me scream every time I perform those last painful reps."

"What kind of routine does Arthur have you on?" I asked.

"It's a killer, a real killer," he said. "Come see for yourself Friday morning."

SERGIO'S THIGH WORKOUT

Friday morning arrived, and true to his word, Sergio showed up with Jones not far behind.

We all walked behind the DeLand High School to a metal building filled with equipment. In those days, that was the only place Jones had to train his subjects.

"Okay Sergio, let's begin with the legs," said Jones in his commanding voice.

Sergio had been personally trained by Jones for several weeks, and he knew what to expect. He walked around nervously looking at the floor and slowly shaking each leg.

"Let's go Sergio," said Jones. "Into the leg press," he pointed. "Get the weight set."

Two large football players put 480 pounds on the leg press machine and adjusted the seat properly.

"Twenty reps, I want twenty reps," Jones said to Sergio, who began leg pressing the enormous weight.

At seventeen repetitions, Sergio looked whipped.

"Rest a few seconds in the lockout," Jones said, "and you'll be able to get three more reps."

Sergio quickly took about five short breaths and squeezed out exactly three more repetitions.

Arthur nodded to the football players, who literally picked Oliva up from the leg press and immediately helped him to the leg extension machine. The weight was set up at 200 pounds, and the goal again was twenty repetitions.

By the tenth repetition, Sergio was in obvious pain. Somehow, with Jones hurling insults about his manhood, Oliva managed another seven or eight repetitions.

Once again Jones signaled the football players, and they pried Sergio from the leg extension and hurried him across the room to the squat racks. The bar had already been loaded to 420 pounds. Three weeks earlier, Arthur noted, Sergio had performed a similar routine, but with less weight, and was unable to perform a single repetition in the squat with 400 pounds. "He'll do 420 today and for at least a dozen reps," Jones confidently predicted.

With 420 pounds on his back, Oliva stepped back from the squat racks and began grinding out the repetitions. The first three reps were extremely hard. In fact, I didn't think he was going to make the second. Somehow he did. Repetitions four through ten seemed a bit easier than the initial ones. He seemed to get into a sort of groove, even though he was breathing and sweating like a steam engine.

Sergio Oliva as he looked in winning the 1981 Professional World Cup in Paris, France.

Repetition eleven went slow, and repetition twelve was very slow. True to Jones's prediction, Sergio failed on his thirteenth rep.

"Take the big plates off," Jones said to the spotters as they helped Oliva back into the racks. "Okay Sergio, any champion bodybuilder ought to be able to squat with 300 pounds."

The return look that Sergio gave Arthur was one of "Boy, would I like to get my hands on you!"

Sergio, however, responded as Jones hoped he would. He shouldered the barbell, backed up, and performed six perfect full squats with 300 pounds. He then returned it to the racks and promptly collapsed on the floor.

I gasped. "Sergio, are you all right?"

"He's all right," Jones said nonchalantly as he finished jotting down some notes on Oliva's workout card. "He needs a little rest before he works his upper body."

Jones allowed Sergio to remain stretched out on the floor under the squat racks for exactly twenty minutes. "Go get Sergio up," he said to me.

I walked over to where Sergio was lying on his back. I knelt down and tapped him on the shoulder. There was no response. His body felt cold and clammy. "Arthur, he looks dead to me," I said.

Just then I noticed Sergio's left eye open. When he saw me looking at him, he smiled. "Arthur wouldn't let me die—at least not until I've finished the workout. Here, help me get up," Sergio said as he reached out his hand.

As Oliva came to his feet, his thighs looked like large columns of black marble. And there was no doubt in my mind that in several days they would be even larger.

HIGH-INTENSITY THIGH CYCLE

The thigh cycle that Sergio performed is the most demanding pre-exhaustion routine ever devised by Arthur Jones. it consists of three exercises:

1. Leg press, immediately followed by
2. Leg extension, immediately followed by
3. Full squat

The key exercise in the thigh cycle is the full squat. The full squat involves many major muscles, namely those of the thighs, buttocks, and lower back. But a problem exists in performing the full squat with a barbell because the muscles of the lower back usually tire before the thighs can be worked thoroughly. If you could pre-exhaust your thighs and then do squats, your lower back, for a short period, would be stronger than your thighs. As a result, when you failed in full squats, you would fail from fatigue in your thighs instead of your lower back.

Here's how you should perform this amazingly intense pre-exhaustion cycle.

Leg press: This exercise is a multiple-joint movement involving the calves, thighs, and buttocks. The primary emphasis, however, is on the quadriceps and hamstrings of the thighs. Don't be afraid to work heavy in this exercise and avoid resting in the locked-out position. Perform fifteen to twenty continuous repetitions in the leg press.

Move quickly from the leg press to the leg extension. As short as three seconds between these two machines will allow significant recovery of your thighs. Thus, it is important on any pre-exhaustion cycle to move from one exercise to the next in *less than three seconds.*

Leg extension: Only the quadriceps are brought into action on this single-joint exercise. Smoothly lift and lower the movement arm for fifteen to twenty repetitions. Be sure to pause briefly at the fully contracted position each time. Your frontal thighs should be "on fire" as you run, with the help of a spotter, to the squat racks.

The first two exercises have effectively pre-exhausted your frontal thighs. Your surrounding muscles are now called into action on the squat to force your pre-exhausted quadriceps to a deeper level of fatigue, as well as to a new level of growth stimulation.

Full squat: The squat is the king of the multi-joint exercises. It involves significant movement around your ankles, knees, hips, and lower back. You won't feel like performing full squats imme-

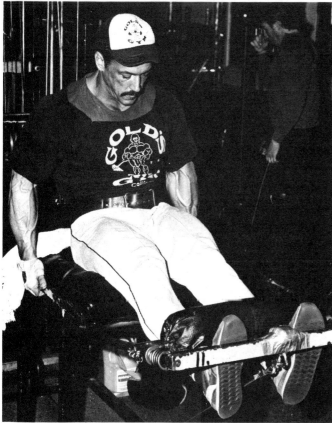

Leg press: Keep the repetitions smooth and continuous.
Leg extension: You won't feel like pausing at the top of this exercise, but do it. Go for the burn!
Full squat: Bend your knees until your hamstrings touch your calves.

diately after the leg press and leg extension, but you'll certainly like the muscular growth that results from it. So do it and complain later.

Take a deep breath—you may need several between each repetition—and lower your buttocks slowly to the bottom. Then immediately return to the erect position. Repeat for fifteen to twenty repetitions.

IMPORTANT ADVICE

The pre-exhaustion thigh cycle takes less than five minutes to perform, but during that time you will perform concentrated work at a level your system is not used to. You are advised to take several break-in workouts to prepare your body for such demands. Even after several workouts, you may still have a tendency to become nauseated afterward. Within four or five workouts, however, your body should become accustomed to the high-intensity demands, and nausea should not recur.

The frequency of such pre-exhaustion cycles for the thighs should be not more than once every four days. Twice-a-week thigh training produces the best growth stimulation in almost all cases.

This high-intensity thigh cycle, however, should not be performed more than twice a week for three weeks in a row. Done properly, it is simply too demanding on your overall recovery ability. After three weeks, try the thigh cycle once a week or once every two weeks. Your normal thigh exercises should be performed during your other training sessions.

Once you've recovered sufficiently from the pre-exhaustion thigh cycle (it usually takes approximately five minutes), you should work your upper body. The routine for your upper body, however, should be shortened to only one set of nine exercises. Thus, your complete workout would resemble the following:

Leg cycle

1. Leg press	2. Leg extension	3. Full squat
		Rest five minutes.

Upper Body Exercises

4. Straight-armed pullover with one dumbbell	6. Press behind neck	10. Triceps extension with one dumbbell
5. Shoulder shrug with barbell	7. Bent-over row	11. Regular chin-up
	8. Bench press	12. Parallel dip
	9. Biceps curl	

When Sergio Oliva first met Arthur Jones, he was used to training his thighs for at least one hour with multiple sets in the traditional fashion. But during his leg workout under Jones's supervision, one cycle of three exercises performed until momentary muscular exhaustion within less than five minutes was all he wanted.

One set of three simple exercises repeated twice a week—try it for larger thighs. You will not be disappointed.

Chapter 16

Chris Dickerson, 1982 Mr. Olympia

Massive Calves

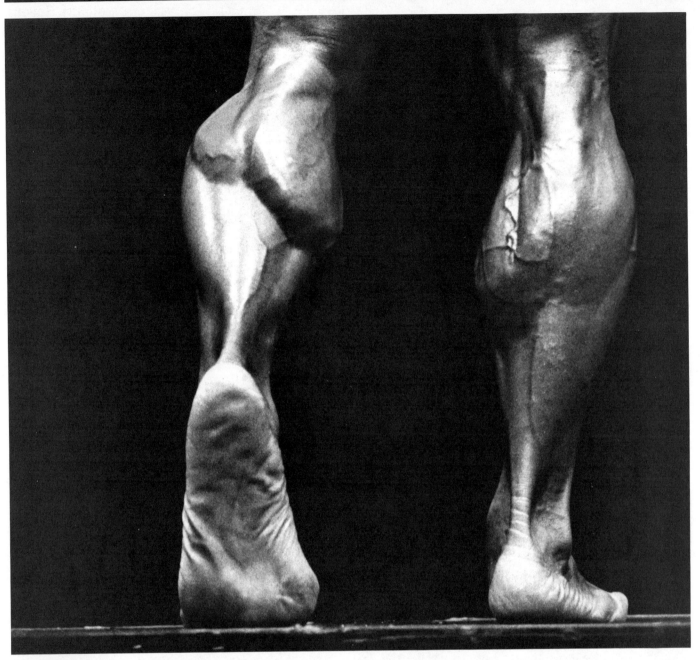

The first bodybuilding contest I ever witnessed was the 1960 Mr. Southern USA contest. I was 16 years old at the time, and I drove 40 miles with a friend to the event at the downtown YMCA in Houston, Texas.

We arrived during the last part of the Olympic weightlifting meet. In those days most bodybuilding shows were held in conjunction with weightlifting competitions. When we walked into the auditorium, there was a powerfully built man on stage performing a press with 325 pounds. I had never seen anyone in person perform a press with even 225 pounds, so 325 was indeed a thrill. That man's name was John Gourgott.

Gourgott was lean and muscular and I knew he must be entered in the Mr.

The calves of Chris Dickerson are the focal point of his championship body.

Southern USA contest. At the conclusion of the lifting, my buddy and I decided that we would sneak backstage and get a close look at the bodybuilders as they warmed up for their competition. Several other teenagers, in fact, had the same idea. We successfully made our way backstage with no problems, and we were not disappointed.

Our first sight was Gourgott stripped to his posing trunks performing chin-ups—not the regular two-armed variety, but one-armed chin-ups. He performed three full repetitions with his right arm and three with his left. To this day, I've never seen another man of his weight (196 pounds) who can duplicate this feat. Needless to say, we were impressed.

John Gourgott's arms were amazingly strong and muscular. Every teenager backstage wanted arms like his. Besides arms, Gourgott had the largest calves I'd ever seen. In fact, my buddy, who was something of a calf enthusiast, kept saying: "Boy, look at his calves. They're better than his arms."

"Mr. Gourgott," I finally said hesitantly, "tell us what you do for your calves."

"Calves? That's simple," he replied. "For bigger calves, just work them as hard as you work your arms." Hurriedly, he put his robe on, smiled, and moved away.

Thirty minutes later, when it came time for Gourgott to pose, he walked on stage, hit a double-armed biceps pose from the front, turned and did the same for the back, and contracted his calves several times. Then he walked off the stage. That was it, three poses at the most.

He won hands down. In fact, in my book he would have won without posing. In 1964 Gourgott almost won the Mr. America title, placing second to Val Vasilef.

John Gourgott impressed me. His answer about working the calves is still etched in my memory, and it's advice that all bodybuilders can profit from: "Train your calves as hard as your arms."

Many bodybuilders fail to train their calves with the same enthusiasm they train their arms. They don't mind training their arms intensely, but for some reason they treat their calves as if they were withered flowers with no future for growth. Hard, brief exercise builds arms—and hard, brief exercise also builds calves.

The following routine will leave a lasting mark on your calves.

HIGH-INTENSITY CALF CYCLE

The calf cycle consists of the following exercises:

1. Leg curl with toes pointed, immediately followed by
2. Standing calf raise, immediately followed by
3. Leg curl with toes pointed, immediately followed by
4. Donkey calf raise

Leg curl with toes pointed: Most trainees perform the normal leg curl with their feet flexed. This stretches the gastroc-soleus muscles of the calves and places more stress on the hamstrings. But by pointing the toes during the movement, some of the stress is taken from the hamstrings and transferred to the gastroc-soleus muscles. Perform twelve leg curls. Keep your toes pointed during both the lifting and the lowering of all repetitions. This pre-exhausts the gastroc-soleus muscles, which are the primary muscles used in the next exercise. Instantly, move to the standing calf raise.

Standing calf raise: You'll need a calf machine of some sort for this movement, or you may perform the exercise with a barbell that has been incorporated into a power rack.

Your form is most important. Since the calf raise involves such a short range of motion, less than six inches, most bodybuilders have a tendency to cheat on their repetitions by moving too fast. To get the maximum degree of muscle fiber involvement, the calf raise should be done *very slowly*. Take a full two seconds to move from the stretched position to the fully contracted position. Count to yourself as you move: one-thousand-and-one, one-thousand-and-two. Pause briefly at the top. Then, slowly lower your heels to the stretched position in four seconds: one-thousand-and-one, one-thousand-and-two, one-thousand-and-three, one-thousand-and-four. Stretch for a second at the bottom, and repeat the movement in the very slow style for fifteen repetitions.

Leg curl with toes pointed: Reduce the weight for the leg curl by approximately 10 percent, and

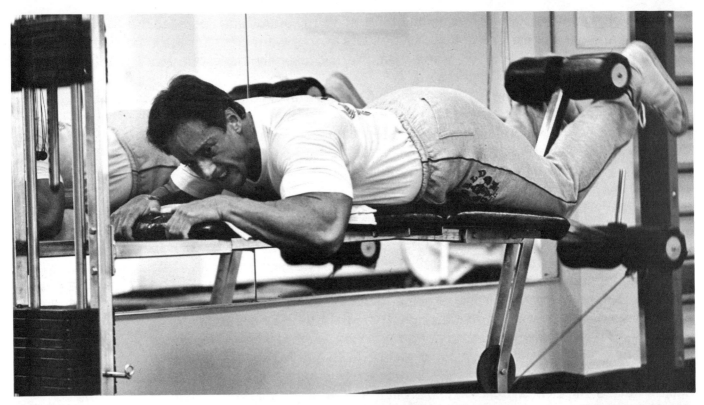

(*Top*) Leg curl with toes pointed: Perform each repetition smoothly and concentrate on involving your calves. (*Bottom Left*) Standing calf raise: Count to yourself as you raise your heels in two seconds and lower your heels in four seconds. (*Bottom Right*) Donkey calf raise; Force your calves to grow by contracting and stretching your gastroc-soleus muscles in a very slow manner.

perform another twelve repetitions. Remember to keep your toes pointed throughout. Then go directly to the donkey calf raise.

Donkey calf raise: This is probably the single best exercise for your calves. You'll need a sturdy block to stand on, a chair to lean against, and a training partner to sit across your hips. With your partner in position and the balls of your feet on the block of wood, lock your knees and keep them locked throughout the exercise. Locking your knees allows you to isolate your gastroc-soleus muscles better. Perform twelve or more *very slow* repetitions, using the two-second positive and four-second negative guidelines described previously. Your calves should now feel like footballs!

FREQUENCY

In all probability, this cycle will make your calves extremely sore. This soreness, however, will not occur until 48 to 72 hours after the workout. You can combat some of the soreness by performing the cycle three days in a row. After three consecutive-day workouts, your calves will need at least 48 hours of rest. Thereafter, best results will occur if you train your lower legs on three non-consecutive days each week.

It is very easy to overwork your calves or any other body part, including your arms. High-intensity exercise is the key factor in muscular growth, but it also makes a severe demand on your body's recovery ability. If your body's recovery ability becomes depleted, then your muscles will not grow— regardless of the intensity of the exercise.

Remember, for the most efficient muscle-building results, your workouts must be high in intensity but brief in duration. And the calf muscles are not an exception.

So for more massive calves, remember the advice of John Gourgott: "Train your calves as hard as your arms." Then back off and rest and permit them to grow.

(Overleaf) Tom Platz tenses his massive calves, which are the result of high-intensity exercise.

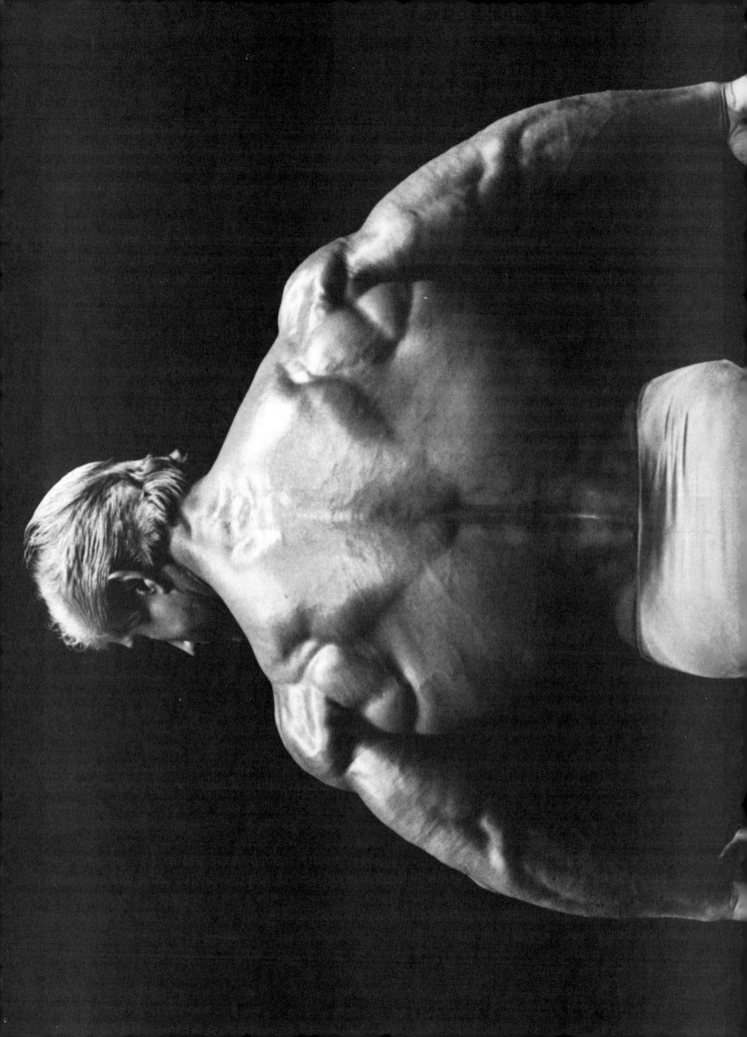

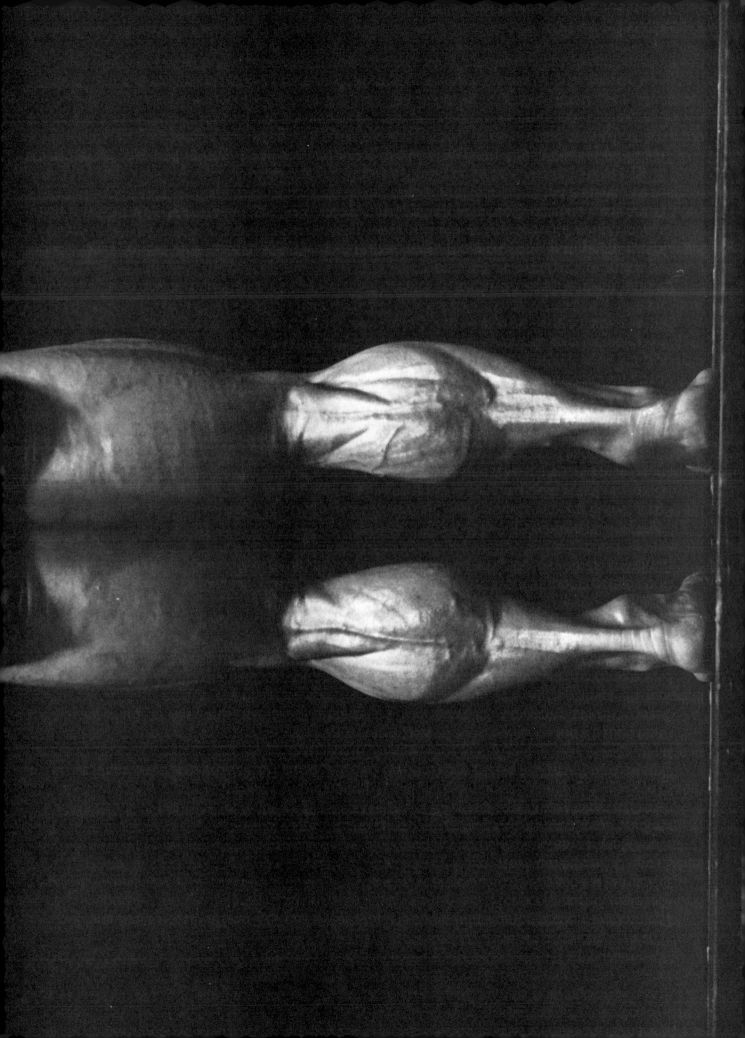

Chapter 17

King-Size Shoulders

For many years, Arthur Jones said he had seen only one man with shoulders 24 inches wide. That was Bill Trumbo who trained at Vic Tanny's Gym in Santa Monica, California, in the late 1940s.

Now that has changed. As of March 2, 1984, Jones has seen two men with 24-inch-wide shoulders. The second man is Scott Wilson.

The Nautilus overhead press machine is worked in a seated position. Parallel handles located by the shoulders are pressed overhead. The distance that the handles are apart, from the outside edge of the left handle to the outside edge of the right handle, is exactly 24 inches. Scott Wilson, when seated in the machine with his elbows by his sides and viewed from the front, has deltoids that completely cover the handles. The

(*Left*) The man with the widest shoulders in bodybuilding: Scott Wilson of San Jose, California.
(*Above*) The shoulders of Scott Wilson cover the ends of the parallel handles on the Nautilus overhead press machine. The distance between the handles is 24 inches.

accompanying picture verifies this fact.

"What's the secret to your incredible deltoids?" I asked Scott during his visit to Nautilus.

"The secret, if there is a secret," replied Scott, "is not in the exercises. I do the same exercises—presses, upright rows, and lateral raises—that everyone else does. The secret, in my opinion, is the style in which I do each deltoid exercise. I make it a habit to perform all my deltoid exercises in super-strict style, especially the dumbbell raises, which I do to the front, side, and back."

"Scott, how far do you carry an exercise?" I asked.

"I've always believed," Scott replied, "in getting everything possible out of each set."

That's good advice from Scott Wilson, the man who is bringing king-size shoulders back into bodybuilding.

CYCLE TRAINING FOR THE SHOULDERS

Here's a pre-exhaustion cycle for your shoulders that's guaranteed to produce results.
1. Bent-over raise with dumbbells, immediately followed by
2. Front raise with dumbbells, immediately followed by
3. Overhead press
   Rest for sixty seconds.
4. Lateral raise with dumbbells, immediately followed by
5. Press behind neck

Bent-over raise with dumbbells: This is a great exercise for your posterior deltoids. With a pair of light dumbbells in your hands, bend over until your torso is parallel to the floor. Let the dumbbells hang. Smoothly raise the dumbbells backward as far as possible. Do not bend your elbows. Keep them locked solidly throughout the movement. Pause in the top position. Lower slowly and repeat for twelve repetitions. Stand up and immediately do front raises.

Front raise with dumbbells: This movement is best performed in an alternate fashion with a slight difference. Start with both arms locked and in front of your body in the fully contracted position of your front deltoids. Lower your right arm slowly to your thigh, then raise it smoothly back to the contracted position. Now lower your left arm and raise it in the same manner. One arm is always holding statically in the contracted position as the other arm performs the complete range of movement. Try to do twelve repetitions with each arm. Move quickly from the front raise to the overhead press.

Overhead press: The bent-over raise and the front raise have effectively pre-exhausted your deltoids. The overhead press goes a step further by using your rested triceps to force your pre-exhausted deltoids to a deeper state of fatigue.

In a standing position, place a barbell in front of your shoulders. Your hands should be shoulder-width apart. Press the barbell smoothly overhead. Do not cheat by bending your legs or arching your back. Lower slowly to your shoulders. Repeat for twelve repetitions.

Walk around, get a drink, or rest for sixty seconds as you ready yourself for the next cycle.

Lateral raise with dumbbells: The lateral raise is performed seated. With light dumbbells in your hands, raise your arms sideways until they are slightly above the horizontal. Pause in the top position. Make sure your palms are facing down and your elbows are locked. Lower the dumbbells slowly to your side. Repeat for twelve repetitions. Move quickly to the press behind neck. Remember, the time between exercises in a pre-exhaustion cycle must be three seconds or less.

Press behind neck: In a standing position, place the barbell behind your neck. Your hands should be about six inches wider than in the overhead press. Press the barbell in a strict manner over your head. Lower slowly behind your neck. Repeat for twelve repetitions. You're permitted to cheat a little on the last repetitions of this exercise, but keep it to a minimum.

COMBINING THE SHOULDER CYCLE WITH OTHER EXERCISES

After the five-exercise shoulder cycle, your deltoids should be thoroughly pumped—pumped to

(*Top*) Bent-over raise with dumbbells: Pause briefly in the top position. Do not bend your arms. (*Bottom Left*) Front raise with dumbbells: Keep your left arm in the contracted position as you raise your right arm. Then keep your right arm straight out as you lower and raise your left arm. (*Bottom Right*) Overhead press: Push the barbell smoothly over your head. Use your rested triceps to force your deltoids to a deeper level of stimulation.

(*Top*) Lateral raise with dumbbells: This is the best shoulder-width builder. Keep your elbows straight as you pause in the contracted position. (*Bottom*) Press behind neck: Start pressing immediately after the lateral raises are completed. Even a three-second rest will destroy the effectiveness of this cycle. The exercise may be done seated, standing, or on a machine.

The wide shoulders of Sergio Oliva.

the point they feel like they're ready to explode. That's an indication that you're stimulating growth in many previously dormant fibers. But to make sure your stimulated deltoids will grow, you've got to keep your other exercise brief.

Yes, you should certainly train your other major muscles during the same workout as your deltoids, but your total sets should number not more than twenty. Subtracting the five exercises in the shoulder cycle from twenty leaves fifteen remaining exercises or sets for your other body parts. That's more than adequate for even the most advanced bodybuilder.

For example, the following routine shows how five exercises can be grouped before the recommended shoulder cycle and how ten exercises can be arranged afterward.

1. Full squat
2. Straight-armed pullover
3. Leg extension
4. Leg curl
5. One-legged calf raise

Shoulder cycle

6. Bent-over raise
7. Front raise
8. Overhead press
9. Lateral raise
10. Press behind neck

11. Regular chin-up
12. Parallel dip
13. Bent-over row
14. Bench press
15. Biceps curl
16. Triceps extension
17. Wrist curl
18. Reverse wrist curl
19. Trunk curl
20. Reverse trunk curl

Such shoulder specialization should continue for three or four weeks but not more than a month. After a month of shoulder specialization, you may specialize on another body part, or you may go back to your basic routine. You may want to concentrate on your shoulders again in three or four months.

Chapter 18

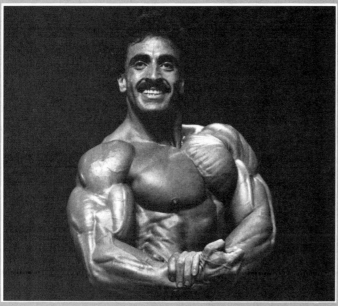

Roy Callendar, Larry Jackson, Samir Bannout and Bertil Fox in their favorite chest poses.

Beefing the Chest

Bertil Fox has more muscle on his body than any other professional bodybuilder today," Chris Lund said to me as he walked into my office, "and this will prove it." Lund had purchased a videotape of the 1983 Mr. Olympia Contest and had brought it along on a recent trip to Florida.

"Come on, Chris," I said in a disbelieving tone. "Several bodybuilders have more muscle than Fox. How about Lee Haney and Lance Dreher? Besides, Fox only placed fifth in the Olympia. How do you explain that?"

"You can see for yourself on the tape," Chris replied confidently.

The only time I had seen Bertil Fox in person was at the 1978 Mr. Universe Contest. Sure, he had won the professional event that year, but in my book Casey

"The key to Bertil Fox's massive chest development," says Chris Lund, "is his muscular strength."

Viator looked much better. Casey competed in the amateur section and placed second to Dave Johns, which should have never happened. Anyway, I'd seen Bertil Fox up close, and he hadn't impressed me that much.

"You keep remembering Fox from six years ago," Chris said. "He was good then. But today he's massive—bloody massive—and cut like nothing you've ever seen!"

"Okay Chris, okay, settle down for gosh sakes. Let's watch the tape."

THE MR. OLYMPIA CONTEST

I put the tape in place, punched "play," and we both settled back into our chairs for a rehash of the 1983 Mr. Olympia Contest in Munich, West Germany.

Jacques Neuville and Jesup Wilkcosz at the 1983 Mr. Olympia

The first five competitors, Jimmy Gaubert, Johnny Fuller, Ed Corney, Hubert Metz, and Jacques Neuville, were all good, but not great. None of them received much applause from the huge audience.

Mohamed Makkawy was next up. He was small but well-built, and a very dynamic poser. He was a certain choice for the top five.

Frank Zane came on with a bang. Soon, however, it was evident he was not in his best shape. Neither Zane nor Makkawy could bring the crowd of 4,500 to its feet.

"Was it a typical Mr. Olympia crowd?" I asked Chris. "They seem to be sitting on their hands."

"They're waiting on the beef," said Chris. "The beef!"

Gerard Buinoud posed eighth and received little response. He was much too mechanical.

Ninth up was Lee Haney. "There's some beef," I remarked.

"Yeah, but it's not equal to Foxy's," said Chris.

Jusup Wilkosz was next, followed by Samir Bannout. Neither was able to ignite the crowd. Bannout, however, had great symmetry and perhaps the best back in the contest.

Lance Dreher followed. Dreher had the mass, but no cuts. He left the audience flat.

Albert Beckles was the opposite to Dreher. Beckles was cut, but didn't seem to have enough mass.

"Foxy's next," said Chris as he straightened up from his slouched position. "Now you'll see some beef."

And I better, I thought to myself. There's little chance that Fox will make a believer out of me.

Bertil Fox lumbered onto the stage like a robot. "He looks like he's carrying the world on his shoulders," I said.

"Just wait 'til he gets into his routine," said Chris.

Fox seemed uneasy at first. Then his music came on. Bam! "Sexual Healing" by Marvin Gaye. Bam! Bam! Evidently the crowd needed some sexual healing, because they roared their approval. Fox responded with his magic smile and a double biceps pose.

"Damn, he does have some beef, doesn't he," I said.

Chris just nodded. "Wait 'til you see his most muscular pose."

After several more poses, Fox turned and jerkily went into his crab pose. The crowd went wild.

"There it is, boy. What did I tell you?" smiled Chris.

Zoom, the camera came in close on Bertil's pecs as he pumped them by moving his arms across his body.

"His pecs must be six inches thick," I commented to Chris.

"At least six inches," he replied as he swayed to the music. "What'd I tell you. Foxy's got mass! And cuts!"

By now the crowd was on its feet. Bertil had them where he wanted them. It was his night and his contest, and he wanted to make the most of it.

Unfortunately, the judges did not agree with the crowd. Fox placed fifth, behind Zane, Haney, Makkawy, and the winner Samir Bannout.

"When Fox was announced in fifth place," remembered Chris, "I was afraid the crowd was going to make a shambles out of the auditorium. I started protecting my cameras in fear of a possible riot."

"What's your opinion on why Fox placed so low?" I asked Chris.

"Well, things like that often happen. You can blame it on the point system. You can blame it on the pre-judging. You can blame it on politics. Or you can say it was just Samir's time to win. But regardless, it was evident to everyone at the contest—and it should be evident to everyone who views the videotape—that Bertil Fox had more muscle on his body than any other man in the contest."

"You're right, Chris," I said, "absolutely right. The videotape made a believer out of me. Bertil Fox has more muscle on his body than any other professional bodybuilder competing today."

THOSE PECS OF FOX'S

That night I couldn't get those pecs of Fox's out of my mind. It brought back thoughts of the tremendously thick chest muscles of George Eiferman, 1948 Mr. America. According to Arthur Jones, Eiferman could take a 10-pound barbell plate, put it between his pecs, contract, and almost succeed at holding it in place. I had visions of Fox actually succeeding at this feat. Wouldn't that make an impressive photo? I thought to myself.

The next day I cornered Chris for some facts about Bertil's training. I knew Chris was a personal friend of Bertil's and had observed him working out in both England and California.

"What's the secret of Fox's massive chest development?" I asked Chris at the first opportunity.

"The secret," replied Lund, "is his strength. He's the strongest bodybuilder I've ever seen train. Where most top bodybuilders handle 35- or 40-pound dumbbells on bent-armed flies, Fox can use 85-pounders with ease. In fact, during one of his workouts in London, an unannounced strongman arrived and proceeded to duplicate what Foxy had just done: ten reps with 85-pound dumbbells in the bent-armed fly. Bertil responded by ripping a pair of 100-pound dumbbells from the racks and performed ten perfect flies with them. The unannounced strongman failed after three or four reps. Foxy loves a good challenge in his workouts, and he refuses to believe that he is not the strongest man in bodybuilding."

"Beside flies," I asked, "what other types of exercises does Fox do?"

"He does incline flies, bench presses, both regular to the chest and a version where he brings the bar down to his neck, pullovers, and dips with weight. When we toured Europe in 1983, Bertil carried his own dipping harness to each gym he visited. He really loves those parallel dips."

ADDING BEEF TO YOUR CHEST

Below is a high-intensity chest routine that we believe would please Bertil Fox.

1. Bent-armed fly, immediately followed by
2. Incline bent-armed fly, immediately followed by
3. Decline bench press to neck
   Rest for several minutes.
4. Bench press, immediately followed by
5. Straight-armed pullover, immediately followed by
6. Dip, negative only

Bent-armed fly: Grasp two heavy dumbbells, sit on a narrow bench, lie back, and curl and press the dumbbells over your chest. This is the starting position. Lower the dumbbells slowly by bending your elbows and shoulders. Keep your hands, elbows, and shoulders in line. Stretch in the bottom, and smoothly move the dumbbells back to the straight-armed position. Repeat.

When you can no longer perform a repetition, sit up, place the dumbbells on the floor, and move quickly to the incline bench.

Incline bent-armed fly: Pick up a slightly lighter pair of dumbbells, stabilize yourself on an incline bench, and press the dumbbells overhead. Lower the dumbbells slowly to either side of your chest, stretch, and press the dumbbells back overhead. Take a deep breath, and repeat until momentary muscular fatigue.

Get off the incline bench and run to the decline bench press rack.

Decline bench press to neck: On this exercise you'll need to use about 50 percent as much weight as you normally handle in the bench press. Be sure to anchor your feet at the top end of the bench. Grasp the barbell slightly wider than the width of your shoulders and bring it over your chest. Lower the barbell slowly, keeping your elbows wide, and lightly touch it to your neck. Press the weight smoothly to the top position, and repeat for eight to twelve repetitions.

At the end of the decline press to the neck, your upper pectorals should be "on fire" and very pumped. You deserve a brief rest and a drink of water. After several minutes of recovery, you should be ready for a set of normal bench presses.

Bench press: Go heavy on the bench, something you can barely do for eight reps. But don't stop at eight if you can do a few more. Do as many as possible.

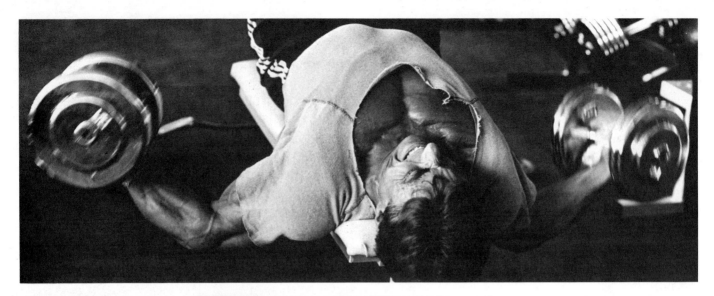

Bent-armed fly: Keep your elbows wide in the stretched position.
Incline bent-armed fly: Do as many strict repetitions as possible.
Decline bench press to neck: This is the best barbell exercise for beefing your chest.

Quickly reposition your body at the other end of the bench, grasp a barbell, and perform a set of straight-armed pullovers.

Straight-armed pullover: Take a deep breath and lower the barbell behind your head. Keep your elbows locked and really try to stretch your rib cage on each repetition. Pull the barbell back to the over-chest position and repeat. Instantly move to the dipping bars.

Dip, negative only: The bench press and the straight-armed pullover should have partially exhausted the upper body. The dip, performed in a negative-only manner, should finish off your chest.

Most stronger bodybuilders will need extra resistance added to their bodyweight to get the best results from negative-only dips. This can be added, in the form of a dumbbell, to a waist belt. Place a chair or sturdy box between the dip bars. Climb to the top position. Straighten your arms, remove your

Bench press: Don't be afraid to work heavy on this exercise.

feet from the chair, and stabilize your body. Lower slowly to the stretched position. This negative movement should take a full eight seconds. Quickly climb back to the top and repeat for eight or twelve repetitions.

It is very important in negative-only dips to stretch fully in the bottom position, climb as fast as possible back to the straight-armed position, and lower your body smoothly under control during each repetition.

USING THE CHEST CYCLE

The chest cycle should be incorporated into your overall workout in a similar way as the shoulder cycle. It is important to keep your overall number of exercises and sets per workout to twenty or fewer.

Straight-armed pullover: One of the best exercises for your ribcage.
Dip, negative only: Climb to the top and take ten seconds to lower your body slowly to a full stretch.

It is equally important to limit your chest specialization to no more than one out of every three months.

Furthermore, it is not recommended that you specialize on your chest and shoulders during the same workout. There is too much overlap between the muscles that compose these body parts.

SIZE AND STRENGTH

It is a well-established fact in exercise physiology that "the size of a muscle is in direct proportion to its strength." To get larger muscles you must make your muscles stronger. Bertil Fox has always trained this way, and so should you.

When Bertil Fox does dumbbell bench presses at the World Gym in Santa Monica, California, it takes four people to hand him his weights. Why? Because each dumbbell weighs 160 pounds!

The chest of Lee Haney.

To add muscle to your chest, to make your chest thicker, or to beef up your pectorals, you must get your muscles stronger. You must force your body to handle heavier and heavier resistance on all your exercises. And of course, make certain that each exercise is done in good form.

Follow the chest cycle as outlined for a month, and no one will ever have to ask you, "Where's the beef?" The beef will be on your chest!

No one has thicker pectorals than Bertil Fox.

Chapter 19

The wide back of Roy Callendar is a result of high-intensity exercise.

Wide, Wide Lats

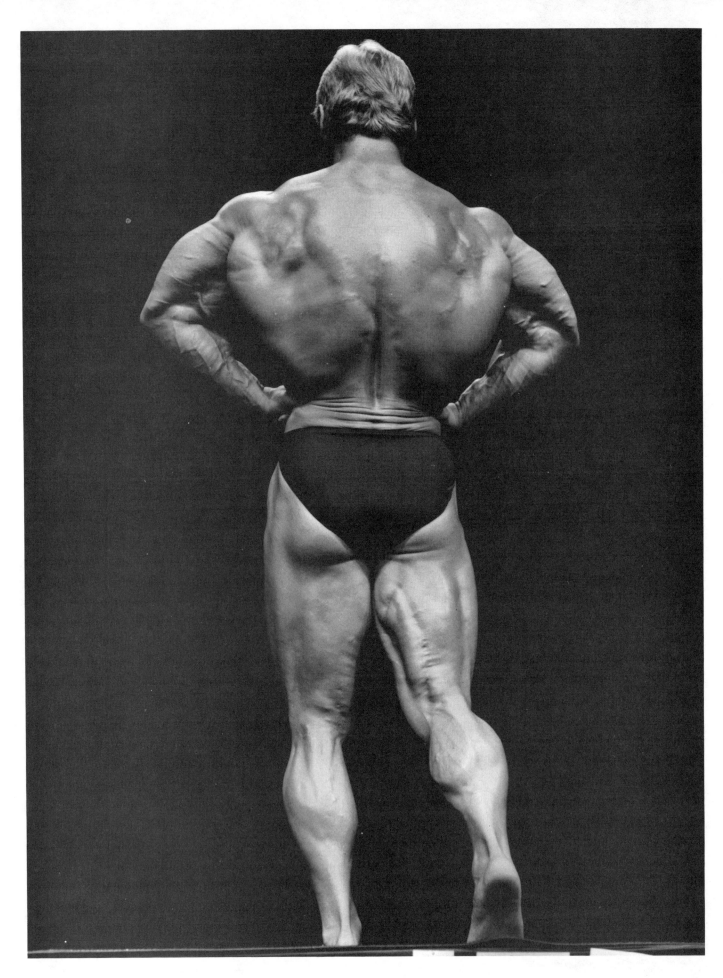

That's Boyer Coe from Lafayette, Louisiana," I said to a buddy of mine as we sat at the back of the auditorium for the start of the 1965 Mr. Texas contest in Tyler. Texas was onc of the few states that allowed out-of-state athletes to enter their bodybuilding championships. But, like a judge said before the contest, "For a Texas bodybuilder *not* to win the Mr. Texas contest would take an outsider who was not only better, but a bunch better."

Boyer Coe was *a bunch better!*

Even at 18 years old and only 185 pounds, the 1965 version of Boyer impressed me more than any other bodybuilder I had ever seen before. In fact, only one man since then has impressed me more, and that was Sergio Oliva.

You be the judge: Does the widest back belong to Lance Dreher, (*page 148*) Lee Haney, or Samir Bannout (*above*)?

Boyer, with his huge, defined arms, deep chest, wide back, and muscular legs, easily defeated a dozen Texans and a couple of competitors from Oklahoma for the title of Mr. Texas 1965.

Almost 20 years later, the thing that stands out in my mind about Boyer Coe is not his great arm or chest development but his wide, wide lats. When Coe walked onto the stage with the other competitors for group comparisons in a relaxed state, he was slightly better than the others from the front and the side. When he turned to the back, however, Boyer was clearly the best "by a bunch."

When viewed from the back, Boyer's lats in a semi-relaxed state actually exceeded the width of his shoulders. Of course, having a minuscule waist didn't hurt the effect either.

"My back development," Boyer says, "won a lot of contests for me, from Mr. Texas to Mr. Universe. I've worked my back hard ever since I was a teenager, and I still emphasize it in my training. You've got

Professional bodybuilding champion Boyer Coe is noted for his complete development.

to train your back hard if you want a winning physique."

HIGH-INTENSITY LAT CYCLE

For the widest possible lats, the following exercises should be done one after the other without rest:

1. Behind neck chin-up, immediately followed by
2. Bent-over row, immediately followed by
3. Bent-armed pullover, immediately followed by
4. Chin-up, negative only

Behind neck chin-up: Hang from a horizontal bar with your hands approximately twelve inches

Behind neck chin-up: Don't get your hands too wide on this exercise or you will limit your range of movement.

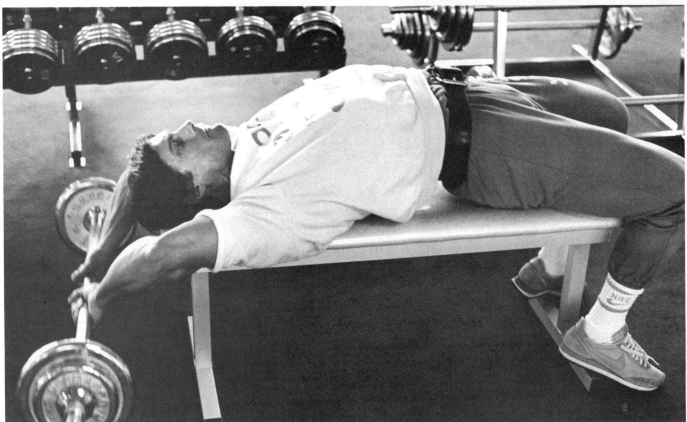

Bent-over row: Using an underhanded grip puts your biceps into the strongest possible position for working your lats.
Chin-up, negative only: Lower your body slowly to the stretched position.
Bent-armed pullover: Keep your arms bent throughout this exercise.

wider than your shoulders. Use an overhand grip. Pull your body up and forward until the bar touches behind your neck. Pause at the top and lower slowly to the bottom position. Repeat for twelve repetitions. If you can perform more than twelve repetitions, you'll need to attach a 25-pound dumbbell to your waist with a belt or a rope.

Bent-over row: In this version of the bent-over row, you should use a narrow underhanded grip. Your hands should be approximately four inches apart. Pull the barbell upward to your navel. Pause, and return slowly to the stretched position. Repeat for twelve repetitions. Immediately do the bent-armed pullover.

Bent-armed pullover: Lie on a high, narrow bench with your head barely off the edge. Anchor your feet securely. Have a spotter hand you a heavy barbell. Your hands should be spaced approx-

Lee Haney relaxes after working his lats.

imately twelve inches apart. The barbell should be resting on your chest in the starting position. Move the barbell over and behind your head and try to touch the floor. Do not straighten your arms; keep them bent. Stretch in the bottom position and smoothly pull the barbell above your face to your chest. Repeat the bent-armed pullover for twelve repetitions. Run to the chinning bar. Remember, it is important to get there in three seconds or less.

Chin-up, negative only: Your lats should be thoroughly pre-exhausted. Your biceps will now force the deeper muscle fibers of your lats to be called into action.

Using a chair for assistance, climb into the top position with your chin over the bar. Use an underhanded grip and space your hands shoulder-width apart. Remove your feet from the chair and lower your body very slowly to the bottom. This slow negative work should take a minimum of eight full

According to Chris Lund, the award for the most complete back development should go to Samir Bannout. (*Above, right and page 156*)

seconds. A training partner should call out the time and pace you during each negative-only repetition. Once at the bottom, instantly climb back to the top position. Repeat the slow lowering for as many repetitions as possible. When you can no longer control your speed of lowering, stop. When you can perform more than twelve repetitions in correct style, add a 25-pound dumbbell to your waist with a belt or rope.

FREQUENCY

The same guidelines that were recommended for the frequency of the shoulder and chest cycles apply to the lat cycle. Work the lat cycle two or three times a week for no more than one out of every three months. And limit your total exercises or sets to twenty.

Wide, wide lats can be yours if you're willing to work harder and briefer.

Chapter 20

Bill Grant and Bertil Fox compare arms at the 1984 World Professional Bodybuilding Championships in Toronto, Canada.

Overdeveloping Your Arms

Of all the champion bodybuilders, Sergio Oliva has come the closest to overdeveloping his arms.

**rms. Massive muscular arms.**

Without arms, as we know them, there would be no baseball biceps or horseshoe triceps. Without arms there would be no need for barbell curls or dumbbell extensions. Without arms the majority of bodybuilders today would have never become interested in developing their muscles.

Arms. Thank goodness for arms. And thank goodness for bodybuilders, for without bodybuilders we would not be able to appreciate massive muscular arms.

No bodybuilder has ever taken his arms for granted. No bodybuilder has ever been completely satisfied with the size and shape of his arms. And no bodybuilder has ever overdeveloped his arms.

The peaked biceps of Albert Beckles.

Many bodybuilders have tried to overdevelop their arms, but none has succeeded. Not Sergio Oliva, not Larry Scott, not Arnold Schwarzenegger, not Lou Ferrigno. But that does not mean overdevelopment is impossible—improbable yes, but not impossible.

To overdevelop your arms would require at least three factors in your favor: (1) superior genetics, (2) proper training, and (3) optimum secondary growth considerations. Secondary growth considerations are discussed in Chapter 10, so this chapter will concern itself with the other two factors.

SUPERIOR GENETICS

Superior genetics means that you have inherited extremely long muscle bellies in your biceps and triceps. Also you would have an excessively large number of muscle fibers in your arms. The longer the muscle belly and the more numerous the fibers, the wider that muscle can be when it is fully developed.

Both length of muscles and number of fibers are completely determined prior to birth and are not subject to improvement. Furthermore, If you are lucky enough to have both, you'll already have large arms—even if you've never done much training.

Champion bodybuilders who have extremely long muscle bellies in their biceps and triceps are Sergio Oliva, Casey Viator, Mike Mentzer, Ray Mentzer, Lance Dreher, and Bertil Fox. Not coincidentally, these men also have, if not the largest, then some of the largest arms in the world.

If you don't have superior genetics, and in all honesty, over 99 percent of the bodybuilders in the world do not, then it simply means you won't be able to overdevelop your arms. But it doesn't mean

One word describes Sergio's arms: MASSIVE!

(*Top*) The heavy-duty arms of Mike Mentzer are an example of extremely long muscle bellies in the biceps, triceps, and forearms. (*Bottom Left*) The highly defined arms and torso of Andreas Cahling. (*Bottom Right*) One repetition chin-up: Take as long as possible to get your chin over the bar. Pause and lower slowly in at least 30 seconds.

you won't be able to improve the size and strength of your biceps and triceps drastically. You can, and quickly!

Whether or not you have superior genetics, there is nothing you can do to change it. What you have inherited is not alterable in a positive direction. All you can do is be realistic in your expectations and make the most of your training. In fact, the training is basically the same, regardless of the genetics.

PROPER TRAINING

Proper training for your arms is based on high-intensity work—or, more specifically, hard, brief exercise for your biceps and triceps. Here's an example of a high-intensity arm cycle that has never failed to produce significant growth.

1. One-repetition chin-up (30 to 60 seconds raising and 30 to 60 seconds lowering), immediately followed by
2. Biceps curl, standing
   Rest for 30 seconds.
3. One-repetition dip (30 to 60 seconds raising and 30 to 60 seconds lowering), immediately followed by
4. Triceps extension with one dumbbell held in both hands

One-repetition chin-up: The objective of the one-repetition chin-up is to make a single repetition as intense and as slow as possible. Such a style of training eliminates momentum, and in doing so it serves to isolate those hurried-through points in your range of movement. Most bodybuilders perform chin-ups in such a fast manner, using excessive body momentum, that the involved muscles are only partially worked. The slow, one-repetition chin-up allows you to isolate the biceps more thoroughly. Effective biceps isolation leads to better and more complete development.

From a hanging, underhand position with arms straight, take as long as possible to get your chin over the bar. Try to move a fraction of an inch and hold, another fraction of an inch and hold, and so on. Remain in each position briefly (without lowering) and move up inch by inch until your chin is above the bar. Have a friend who has a watch with a second hand call out the time in seconds (5, 10, 15, 20) to you as the exercise progresses. Once you've achieved the top position, lower yourself in exactly the same manner. Again, a friend or training partner should call out your time in seconds. Begin this movement with 30 seconds up and 30 seconds down. Add 5 seconds to both the positive and negative phases each workout. When you can perform 60 seconds up and 60 seconds down, attach a 25-pound dumbbell around your waist to make the exercise harder. After this unique chin-up, run to the biceps curl.

Biceps curl, standing: Doing curls immediately after the one-repetition chin-up will reduce your strength in the barbell curl approximately 50 percent. In other words, you should use about half the resistance you would normally handle for eight to twelve repetitions.

Grasp the barbell with an underhand grip and stand erect. Curl the barbell smoothly in the strictest possible form. Lower slowly to the bottom. Repeat in perfect form for at least eight repetitions. Loosen your form and do two more repetitions. Cheat just enough to get past the sticking point. Your spotter should now step in and give you two forced repetitions. In forced repetitions, he helps you on the positive movement and you lower it under control.

Your biceps should now be under intense pain, but you still need to complete two negative-only repetitions. Allow your partner to lift the barbell to the top position for you. Now lower it to the bottom very slowly in at least 8 seconds. Get one more negative-only repetition in this manner and give it your absolute all.

Have a quick drink of water, if you'd like, and get ready to work your triceps.

One-repetition dip: The one-repetition dip is performed in a similar fashion to the one-repetition chin-up. Start the dip in the bottom, stretched position. Take 30 to 60 seconds to move to the top and an equal amount of time to lower. Your training partner should make sure that he paces you properly by

calling out your raising and lowering times in seconds. Next is the triceps extension.

Triceps extension: Run to the nearest bench, sit down, grasp one dumbbell in both hands, and start performing triceps extensions. Keep your upper arms in a vertical position with your elbows stabilized by your ears. Slowly lower and raise the dumbbell behind your head for at least eight repetitions. When you can no longer do the repetitions strictly, cheat two more up and concentrate on the lowering. Then have your spotter give you two forced repetitions, which are followed by two negative-only repetitions. Don't give up until you've squeezed every bit of strength out of your triceps. And don't be surprised if, 60 seconds after this exercise is completed, your arms are pumped to a degree you've been unable to achieve in the past.

Biceps curl, standing: Start the curl immediately after the chin-up. Make your biceps beg for mercy.
Triceps extension: Do as many repetitions as possible, plus two forced repetitions and two negative-only repetitions.

MAXIMIZING RESULTS

For maximum results, do only one set of each of the four exercises in the arm cycle. Train your arms in this fashion three times a week, and work your arms toward the end of the overall routine. Do not continue to work your arms in this manner for longer than one month. After one month, return to your basic routine or specialize on another body part. You may return to the arm cycle in three or four months.

Another important consideration in building bigger arms is your ability to record each of your workouts accurately. Records are necessary in any progressive training. Include the date, time of day, order of exercises, resistance, repetitions, sets, and overall training time. This recording is often best accomplished immediately after each exercise or cycle by a training partner.

One-repetition dip: Move slowly up and move slowly down.

A reliable training partner can add consistency and motivation to your workouts. He tells you to slow down, to quit cheating, to do the last repetition, to hustle quickly from one exercise to the next, and to do many other things that make each exercise harder and more productive. So choose your training partner wisely.

I've personally trained many champion bodybuilders on the recommended arm routine. Without exception, all of them have achieved significant results. Yes, it's very grueling, but it works.

As an interesting side note, of the bodybuilders I've trained, only one was able to take a full 60 seconds up and 60 seconds down on the one-repetition chin-up and dip the first time he tried it. Furthermore, he performed this grueling feat, not at the beginning of the workout when it's easier to do, but at the end of his routine. That one man was Boyer Coe!

A SUBSTITUTE ARM ROUTINE

Some bodybuilders are not advanced enough to perform the one-repetition chin-up and the one-repetition dip effectively. Initially, they will not be able to take at least 30 seconds up and 30 seconds down in those two exercises. This substitute arm routine is recommended for those trainees.

1. Biceps curl against a post, immediately followed by
2. Close-grip pulldown on lat machine
   Rest for 30 seconds
3. Triceps pressdown on lat machine, immediately followed by
4. Close-grip bench press

Biceps curl against a post: Performed strictly, this exercise prevents body sway in curling. It isolates the biceps much better than normal curling styles.

First, you'll need a sturdy vertical post to rest your torso against. Grasp a moderately heavy barbell with an underhanded, shoulder-width grip, and stand erect with your back to the post. Your feet should be about twelve inches from the post as you lean back into it. Keep your buttocks and upper back in contact with the post during the entire set.

Curl the barbell smoothly to the top. Lower slowly to the bottom. Repeat for eight to twelve repetitions. Move quickly to the pulldowns.

Close-grip pulldown on lat machine: Stabilize yourself under the pulldown bar. Grasp the bar with an underhanded grip. Your hands should be approximately four inches apart. Pull the bar to your chest. Pause, and return slowly to the stretched position. Repeat in good form for as many repetitions as possible.

Your biceps should be burning as you prepare to work your triceps.

Triceps pressdown on lat machine: You'll get better contraction of the triceps on this exercise if you use a parallel grip, which can be accomplished by looping a towel around the bar. Grasp each end of the towel and move your elbows to a stable position by your waist. Do not move your elbows.

Press downward on the towel and straighten your arms. In the fully contracted position, your hands should be about six inches away from your upper thighs. Keeping your hands away from your thighs when your arms are straight makes the exercise harder. Bring your hands back to shoulder level and repeat the pressdown for eight to twelve repetitions. Move immediately to the close-grip bench press.

Close-grip bench press: Lie on a flat bench. Grasp a barbell with your hands approximately six inches apart. Lower the barbell to your chest and press it back to the straight-armed position. Repeat for as many repetitions as possible.

Use this arm routine three times a week for three consecutive weeks. Anytime you can do more than twelve repetitions on an exercise, add 5 percent more resistance at the next workout. Get as strong as possible.

After three weeks of such training, go back and try the one-repetition chin-up and dip. I'll be surprised if you cannot perform them now.

(Top Left) Biceps curl against a post: Keep your buttocks and upper back against the post during both the positive and negative phases. (*Top Right*) Close-grip bench press: With a narrow grip, press the barbell smoothly. Grind out as many repetitions as you can. (*Bottom Left*) Close-grip pulldown on lat machine: Pull the bar smoothly to your chest. (*Bottom Right*) Triceps pressdown on lat machine: Do not move your elbows. Keep them stable by your sides. Only your hands and forearms should move.

THE OVERDEVELOPMENT CHALLENGE

If overdevelopment of the arms ever occurs, it will occur as a result of superior genetics combined with hard, slow, strict, brief, supervised exercise. Try the recommended arm cycle for one month, and watch your arms grow. Who knows? You just may be the first man with overdeveloped arms.

The thick triceps of Casey Viator.

Bertil Fox and Sergio Oliva in a battle of mass and muscularity.
(*Overleaf*) Bertil Fox flexes his awesome arm at the Mr. Olympia Contest.

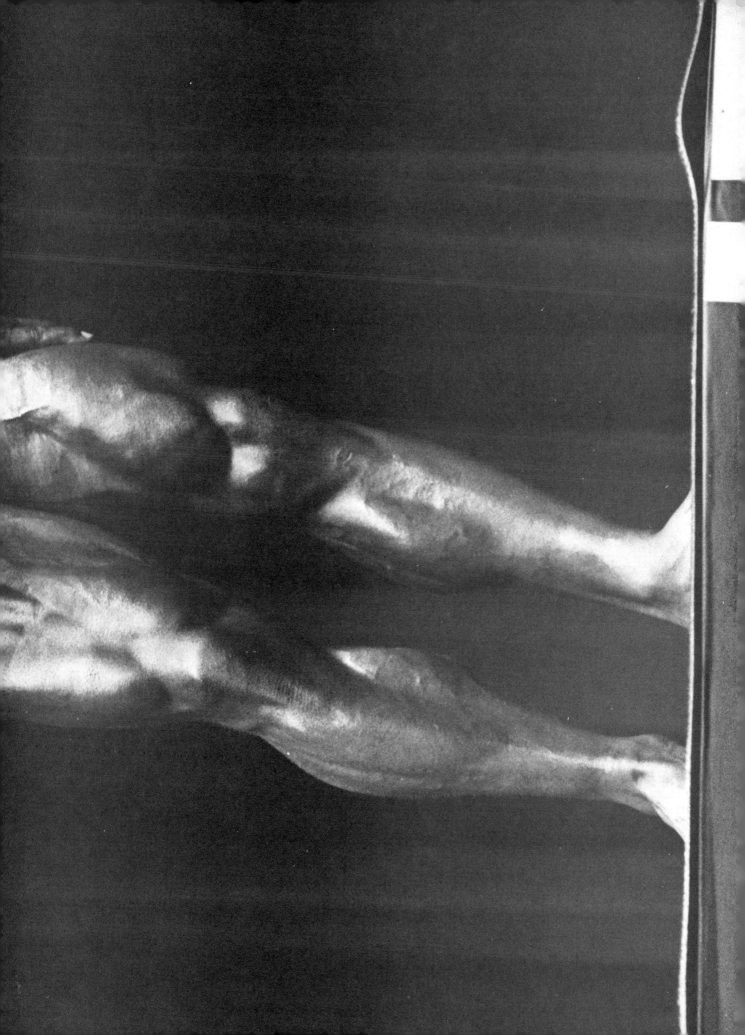

Chapter 21

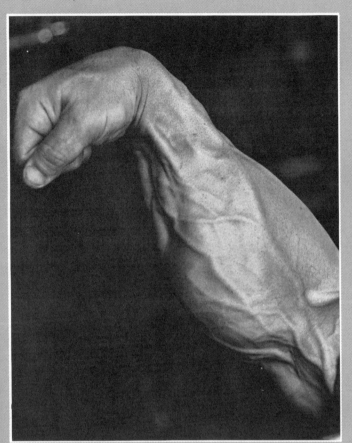
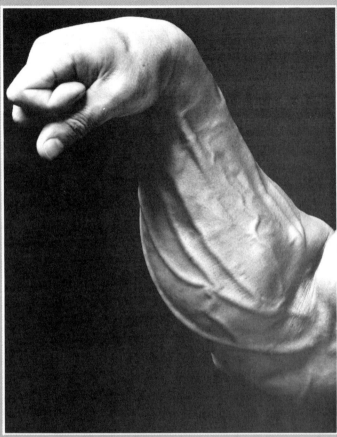

Forearms
of Steel

Casey Viator. What comes to your mind when his name is mentioned?

If you're a typical bodybuilder, Casey's name probably brings to your mind the image of massive, rock-hard muscles.

I trained with and around Casey Viator throughout the 1970s. Sure, Casey has massive, rock-hard muscles. But when I hear his name what pops into my mind are his forearms. Casey's most impressive body part, in my opinion, are his unbelievably thick forearms.

Most bodybuilders don't appreciate well-developed forearms until they see them up close. When you see Casey up close, you cannot take your eyes off his massive forearms. They hang like clusters of grapes from his elbows.

(*Opposite Left*) The huge forearm of Casey Viator.
(*Opposite Right*) The defined forearm of Scott Wilson.
(*Above*) Notice the amazing length of Sergio's forearm flexor muscles.

Casey Viator is noted for his impressive forearms.

At a bodyweight of 215 pounds, Casey's forearm circumference is 15½ inches. I've seen two men, Sergio Oliva and Ray Mentzer, with as large or slightly larger forearms. But Sergio, 15½ inches at 233 pounds, and Ray, 15⁹⁄₁₆ inches at 260 pounds, are both significantly heavier than Casey. Casey's forearm size in relationship to his bodyweight is the primary reason his forearms are more impressive than those of Sergio or Ray.

While Casey Viator has the most impressive forearms I've ever seen, the most defined forearms I've ever seen belong to Scott Wilson.

Scott first visited Nautilus Sports/Medical Industries on February 26, 1984. He had competed in a professional bodybuilding contest in Toronto, Canada, just the day before, so he was in lean condition.

When Scott arrived with Chris Lund at Orlando International Airport, he was wearing white tennis shoes, jeans, and a heavy blue sweatshirt with sleeves cut off at the elbows. As he approached me in the waiting room, he was carrying a bag in each hand. All I could see were two, huge, tan forearms that looked as if they had been assembled with bundles of steel cables. Scott's entire midsection seemed to be hidden behind his highly defined forearms.

"Shake hands with Scott Wilson," Chris said to me as I stuck out my measly forearm and hand.

"That's a pretty fair forearm you have there, Scott," I said as I shook his hand.

"Yeah," said Chris, "Scott's been getting all kinds of strange stares from the porters, agents, flight personnel, and passengers ever since we left Toronto this morning. One guy even accused him of smuggling heroin in his forearms."

"Well, if that guy's right," I smiled, "then Scott's forearms must be worth several million dollars."

"I hate to disappoint you fellows," Scott replied, "but my forearms are only muscle and blood, skin and bones!"

But certainly they are not your average muscle and blood, skin and bones.

To build a pair of forearms like Scott Wilson's or Casey Viator's requires the same factors discussed in the previous chapter on arms. You must have long muscle bellies in your forearms, and you must train these muscles intensely and briefly. Even if you don't have a genetic makeup similar to Scott or Casey, you can still build forearms you can be proud of with the right exercise.

HIGH-INTENSITY FOREARM CYCLE

Cycle training for your forearms is a must. Because of the short range of movement of the involved muscles, it is necessary to perform four exercises in a row for thorough stimulation of growth in your forearms. Let's examine the recommended sequence.

1. Wrist curl, immediately followed by
2. Finger curl, immediately followed by
3. Reverse wrist curl, immediately followed by
4. Reverse curl, standing

Wrist curl: Grasp a barbell with a palms-up grip. Rest your forearms on your thighs and the back of your hands against your knees, and be seated. Your forearms may also be placed on a declined bench for better stability. Lean forward until the angle between your upper arms and forearms is less than 90 degrees. This allows you to isolate your forearms more completely. Curl your hands smoothly and contract your forearm muscles. Pause, and lower the barbell slowly. Do not allow your forearms or torso to move. Do not extend your fingers. Keep the bar in the palm of your hands. Repeat for twelve repetitions. Reduce the barbell approximately 25 percent and immediately start the finger curl.

Finger curl: Assume the same position as for the wrist curl. Instead of moving your hands and flexing your wrists, simply extend your fingers. Curl the bar back to your hands with your fingers, and repeat for twelve repetitions. Place the barbell on the floor, lighten the weight, and do the reverse wrist curl.

Reverse wrist curl: Assume the same position as for the wrist curl, except reverse your grip. Move the backs of your hands upward. Pause in the top position. Lower slowly to the down position. Repeat for twelve repetitions. Move quickly to a heavier barbell for the reverse curl.

Reverse curl: This exercise will finish off your fatigued forearms. Grasp a barbell with a palms-

Finger curl: Extend and curl fingers.
(*Inset*) Wrist curl: Try to isolate your forearms as much as possible.

Reverse wrist curl: This is the best exercise for the extensor muscles on the back of your forearm.
Reverse curl: Use your upper arms to force your forearms to grow larger and stronger.

down grip and stand erect. Stabilize your elbows against your sides and keep them there throughout the exercise. Reverse curl the barbell. Lower slowly back to the bottom. Repeat for twelve repetitions.

FOREARM HINTS

Work your forearms toward the end of your routine immediately after your upper arms. It would be a mistake to include more than one set of the forearm cycle in any one workout. Doing more than you need, or more than your muscles can take, can only hinder your progress.

Train your forearms in the high-intensity manner three times a week for a month, and you'll be pleasantly surprised by their improvement. With a little help from genetics, you may soon give Casey Viator and Scott Wilson a run for their money.

The "Mr. Forearms" title goes to Casey Viator.

Chapter 22

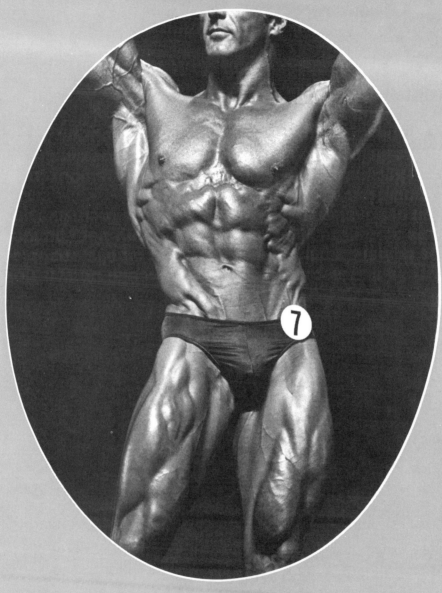

Frank Zane displays his magic midsection.

Midsection Magic

Dennis Tinerino is known for his perfectly paired abdominals.

Frank Zane," I said to Chris Lund, "has the most symmetrical midsection in professional bodybuilding."

"What about Johnny Fuller?" said Chris. "Now there's a man with abdominals. Or how about Bill Grant? His abs are paired to perfection."

"Yeah, Fuller has abs, but they're almost too thick for the rest of his body," I replied. "And Grant, well he's closer to Zane, but still there's something missing. Grant just doesn't have that finely chiseled look to his midsection that Zane has. Here, let's look at some of the prints from last year's Mr. Olympia."

We shuffled through a stack of photos from the contest and pulled out those of Zane.

The midsection of Bill Grant adds to his muscular physique.

"You're right," Chris commented, "look at the tie-in Frank has among his upper abdominals, lower pecs, and serratus anteriors; and likewise the tie-in between his lower abdominals and external obliques. It's magic, pure magic!"

"Maybe we could say Frank Zane has *midsection magic*," I suggested.

"We could at that," agreed Lund, "we could at that. Midsection magic—I like it."

"You know, Chris, I believe we've just discovered the ideal title for the last chapter: Midsection Magic."

GETTING LEAN
One of the most important factors in developing midsection magic is your fatness or leanness.

Lee Haney displays a tight waistline.

Fatness and leanness are opposites. Fatness describes an abundance of body fat. Leanness concerns a lack of body fat. Naturally, leanness is a prerequisite for success in a bodybuilding contest, and a high degree of leanness is necessary for midsection magic.

It is possible to have a great set of abdominals and obliques that no one ever notices, If they are covered by a thick layer of fat. This is the situation with many bodybuilders, because the midsection is the primary storage area for fat.

Most of the fat an average man has is located between his skin and his muscles all over his body. Thin layers are located around the feet, hands, and head. The layers increase as we move toward the body's core. The upper arms and thighs, for example, have thicker layers than do the forearms and calves. The thickest layers of fat on a man's body are located on his waist, usually around the navel and

---

Frank Zane's midsection is a result of discipline, motivation, and patience.

over the sides between the lower ribs and pelvic girdle.

Fat deposition and fat reduction are ordered processes. A typical bodybuilder might deposit fat first on the sides of his waist. Second, it might go over the navel area; then the hips and chest; then the upper arms and thighs; and finally the calves, forearms, hands, feet, and head. When he starts reducing fat, it comes off in reverse: first from the head, feet, hands, forearms, and calves; then the thighs and upper arms; followed by the chest and hips; and finally the navel area and sides.

Certain people may have a slightly different ordering of favorite fat-storage spots. But there is most definitely an ordering, and that ordering is genetically determined and not subject to change.

It should be obvious from the above discussion that losing fat from a specific part of your body, often called "spot reduction," is not possible. Fat is reduced from all over your body, but in dispropor-

The thick abdominals of Johnny Fuller.
Samir Bannout has little fat around his navel area.

tionate amounts.

Losing fat is a result of your caloric intake and caloric output. Quite simply, your caloric intake must be less than your caloric output. You must eat fewer calories than you expend on a daily basis.

Most bodybuilders trying to become leaner should limit their total food intake to 1,500 to 1,800 calories per day. The most efficient fat-loss diet is composed of three or four balanced meals per day. Each meal should contain 400 to 500 calories and be balanced as follows: carbohydrates, 55 percent; fats, 30 percent; and proteins, 15 percent.

Besides limiting your dietary calories, the other important factor in acquiring midsection magic is proper exercise. Even though you may be lean, you still must have symmetrical development of your midsection muscles. The most important midsection muscles are the rectus abdominis and external and internal obliques. Before the recommended exercises are discussed, it is important to dispel several misconceptions.

MIDSECTION MISCONCEPTIONS

The belief that sit-ups and leg raises are abdominal exercises is a misconception. These movements primarily work your hip flexors or iliopsoas muscles. The hip flexors connect the upper femur bones of your thighs to the lower lumbar region of your spine. When these muscles contract, they pull your upper body to a sitting position, or they pull your thighs toward your chest, as in a leg raise. Your rectus abdominis is only mildly involved in a traditional sit-up and leg raise.

The primary function of your rectus abdominis is to shorten the distance between the lower portion of your sternum and your pelvic girdle. This movement is accomplished by a trunk curl and a reverse trunk curl.

Another common misconception among bodybuilders is that the midsection should be worked with more repetitions than other body parts. Many bodybuilders perform sit-ups and leg raises by the hundreds in a mistaken belief that they will assist in burning fat and defining the waistline. Exercise for the midsection has little effect on fat loss in the waist. It cannot be emphasized too often that spot reduction is *not* possible. The abdominals and the obliques should be treated as any other muscle group. They should be subjected to hard, brief, progressive exercise.

HIGH-INTENSITY MIDSECTION CYCLE

Four exercises compose the midsection cycle:
1. Side bend, immediately followed by
2. Trunk curl, immediately followed by
3. Reverse trunk curl, immediately followed by
4. Heel-high trunk curl

Side bend: Grasp a heavy dumbbell in your right hand. Stand erect and place your left hand on top of your head. Bend laterally to your right. This bending stretches your left obliques. Return smoothly to the erect position. Repeat the bending to your right for twelve repetitions. Switch the dumbbell to your left hand and perform twelve side bends to your left side.

Trunk curl: This exercise activates your rectus abdominis by relaxing your iliopsoas muscles. Lie face up on the floor with your hands behind your head. Keep your chin on your chest. Bring your heels up close to your buttocks and spread your knees. Do not anchor your feet under anything, and don't have a partner hold your knees down. Anchoring your feet involves the iliopsoas.

Try to curl your trunk smoothly to a sitting position. Only one-third of a standard sit-up can be performed in this fashion. Pause in the contracted position and lower your trunk slowly to the floor. Repeat for twelve repetitions. When twelve or more repetitions can be done, add a barbell plate behind your head. Move quickly to the reverse trunk curl.

Side bend: Use a heavy dumbbell in this movement.
Trunk curl: Try to get your shoulders off the floor as much as possible.
Reverse trunk curl: Keep your knees on your chest. Only your buttocks and pelvic area should move.

Reverse trunk curl: This exercise also works your rectus abdominis, but from the opposite direction. Lie face up on the floor with your hands on either side of your hips. Bring your thighs on your chest so your knees and hips are in a flexed position. Curl your pelvic area toward your chest by lifting your buttocks and lower back. Pause in the contracted position. Lower your buttocks to the floor. Repeat for twelve repetitions.

The trunk curl and reverse trunk curl, performed back-to-back, will cause your abdominals to contract as never before. You may even experience temporary muscle cramps during the reverse movement, especially if your abdominals are weak. Don't be concerned. This is simply an indication that you're involving fibers you have not previously worked.

Heel-high trunk curl: Lie on the floor and place your calves on the top of a bench. Position

Heel-high trunk curl: Make your abdominals work harder by keeping the body sway to a minimum.

yourself so your thighs are at a 45-degree angle with the floor. Place your hands behind your head and your chin on your chest. Curl your trunk to your knees. Pause, and lower slowly to the floor. Repeat for twelve repetitions. When you can perform more than twelve repetitions, make the movement harder by putting a barbell plate behind your head. You may also perform the exercise by twisting at the top, which involves more of your obliques in the movement.

DISCIPLINE AND PATIENCE

That's it for your midsection: one set of each of four exercises performed in succession until momentary muscular exhaustion. Don't make the mistake of training your midsection more frequently or with higher repetitions than your other muscles. Remember, spot reduction of body fat is not

Ron Tuefel, a weight-class winner in three consecutive Mr. America contests, is known for his thick, well-defined abdominals.

possible.

If you have too much fat around your waistline, then you probably also have too much fat over the rest of your body. Adhere to a balanced, lower-calorie diet to reduce your percentage of body fat, and train your entire body in the prescribed, high-intensity fashion.

Frank Zane didn't produce his magic midsection overnight. Neither will you. Take it one day at a time and don't give up.

Midsection magic can be yours. But it takes discipline and patience, as well as the proper know-how.

This chapter has given you the know-how. You must supply the discipline and patience.

Frank Zane, three-time winner of Mr. Olympia, understands the proper balance between diet and exercise.

189

Conclusion

The road that leads to a massive muscular body is not easy to travel. It is demanding and there are many pitfalls, roadblocks, and dead-ends along the way. As a result, many bodybuilders never reach their destinations. Or if they do, it takes them five times longer than it should have.

      High-Intensity Bodybuilding makes your journey faster and more efficient. It combats and removes the pitfalls, roadblocks, and deadends that are lurking beyond every curve. All you have to do is understand and apply the signposts along the way:

Do everything possible to isolate and work each large muscle group to exhaustion.

1. Train harder, but briefer.
2. Exercise progressively.
3. Control the resistance.
4. Accentuate the negative.
5. Work your largest muscles first.
6. Do not split your routine.
7. Train with a partner.
8. Pre-exhaust your weaknesses.
9. Specialize wisely, but infrequently.
10. Keep accurate records.

High-intensity training is brutally hard work. The bodybuilding results, however, are well worth the effort.

The battle cry of 52-year-old Albert Beckles as he wins the 1984 World Professional Bodybuilding Championships is *Don't Give Up!* Apply it to your training now.

For a free catalog of fitness books, please send a self-addressed, stamped envelope to Dr. Ellington Darden, Darden Research Corporation, P.O. Box 1016, Lake Helen, FL 32744.